Numenéra

NINTH WORLD BESTIARY 2

CREDITS

Writer/Designer	Bruce R. Cordell
Additional Design	Dennis Detwiller
Creative Director	Monte Cook
Managing Editor	Dennis Detwiller
Editor	Ray Vallese
Proofreader	Gina Williams
Cover Artist	Kieran Yanner
Graphic Designer	Bear Weiter
Additional Layout	Zoa Smalley

Artists

Jacob Atienza, Christopher Burdett, Vincent Coviello, Sam Cullum, Dreamstime.com, Felipe Escobar, Inkognit, Guido Kuip, Kezrek Laczin, Brandon Leach, Eric Lofgren, Anton Kagounkin Magdalina, Patrick McEvoy, Brynn Metheney, Giorgio De Michele (Erebus), Irina Nordsol, Rebecca On, Mirco Paganessi, Grzegorz Pedrycz, John Petersen, Roberto Pitturru, Scott Purdy, Eric Quigley, Nick Russell, Lie Setiawan, Joe Slucher, Zoa Smalley, Kim Sokol, Cyril Terpent, Cory Trego-Erdner, Tiffany Turrill, Shane Tyree, Chris Waller, Cathy Wilkins, Ben Wootten, Kieran Yanner

Monte Cook Games Editorial Board

Scott C. Bourgeois, David Wilson Brown, Eric Coates, Gareth Hodges, Mila Irek, Jeremy Land, Laura Wilkinson, Marina Wold, George Ziets

As we agree with the growing consensus that "they" can and should be used as a gender-neutral, singular English language pronoun when one is needed, we have adopted that as the style in our products. If you see this grammatical construction, it is intentional.

MonteCook
Games

TABLE OF CONTENTS

Children know that monsters seep in from dreams, leak up from dank wells, and dart through nighttime forests. When you're nine years old, it's obvious. And after all, it's all true, as victims of carnivorous colors, jiraskars, broken hounds, and cannibalistic nildirs well know.

Many places offer sanctuary in the Ninth World. That's why so many people never travel far. If your village is safe, why go exploring beyond that weird hill to the west, when everyone who's ever gone over there has never returned? Obviously something got them. Probably a creature more demonic than natural, as the village gossip or local storyteller is happy to describe. Here are some of the stories they tell:

There is a creature that understands us better than we understand ourselves. It emulates what humans love and want most in order to exploit that trust and eventually kidnap their victims so they can be dissected by alien minds.

Creatures of endless hunger slip between the folds of reality to hunt their next meal. Mutated and hungry, these planar cannibals hunt humans, abhumans, and other beings with knowledge that seasons the flesh, though anyone alive—or recently so—will do.

Another creature announces itself with a tremor. A rumbling. Then, far more quickly than you might expect (if you were smart enough to realize that the rumbling was the approach of a large beast), a terrible but beautiful shape emerges from the tall trees, a creature as colorful as a jungle flower but burgeoning with teeth and hunger and death.

One tribe of abhumans has normal heads. Their bodies, however, are anything but; they're a jumble of two to four other bodies—sometimes human, sometimes not—fused together to create an awkward patchwork of legs, arms, limbs of weird creatures, and even a few half-fused but inactive heads.

The spiral shell of these creatures' bodies is partly translucent, revealing a mass of gelatinous slime wrapped along the tight interior path. Emerging from the shell are spiny water wings, a whipping tail, and a hideous face whose gaze drinks minds.

All these beasts and many more live in the Ninth World. If you travel long enough and far enough, perhaps you will encounter these creatures of which fabulists speak, learn their names, and come away with stories of your own that end with *you* getting the better of the beast instead of the other way around. Stories that help to quell a nine-year-old's fear of monsters, and replace it with wonder.

Throughout this book, you'll see page references to various items accompanied by this symbol. These are page references to the *Numenera* corebook, where you can find additional details about that item, place, creature, or concept. It isn't necessary to look up the references in the corebook; it's an optional way to learn more about the Ninth World and provide additional information to your players.

PART 1:
USING NUMENERA CREATURES

USING NUMENERA CREATURES

The concept of a demon—a spiritually evil entity—is a label for threats that can't be understood.

The vast majority of people living in the Ninth World don't have a grasp of its expanse. That's because most people are isolated, and many don't ever travel more than a few miles from the place they were born for the entirety of their lives. They have a very narrow view of existence and how the world works. They typically don't understand or at least appreciate the significance of landscape ecology or the wider life cycles of various creatures and automatons that share the world with them.

DEMONIC FALLACY

Player characters, many Aeon Priests, and similar explorers gain a much wider exposure to different kinds of creatures found in the Ninth World. For example, what normal people might describe simply as an otherworldly horror, a PC might know as a creature called a jiraskar. But for people living in a small village being menaced by this colorful predator, the jiraskar is simply a demon.

Common people don't have the knowledge or perspective to imagine that a thing nearly 20 feet (6 m) tall that hungers for flesh is anything other than a supernatural beast of pure evil. The truth is that jiraskars are simply apex predators, and fierce ones at that. Despite their size, they are animals. But the dangers that these creatures pose make the Ninth Worlders' perceptions understandable. The concept of a demon—a spiritually evil entity—is a label for threats that can't be understood. To lump all creatures that hunger for flesh and hunt humans together as demons is clearly simplistic. Worse, doing so probably robs locals of potential strategies for dealing with such a creature. An animal can be dealt with. But a demon?

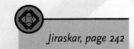

Jiraskar, page 242

> *Even a single creature can be perceived completely differently, depending on the location where it's encountered.*

SCOURGE, COMPANION, OR DELICACY

If the average Ninth Worlder had a wider perspective, they might gain a similar appreciation for the variation that exists across the continent. Even a single creature can be perceived completely differently, depending on the location where it's encountered.

Let's continue with our jiraskar example. In the Westwood, the term "demon" is commonly applied to this monster, which makes its presence known first with a rumbling. Then, far more quickly than might be expected, a terrible but beautiful shape emerges from the tall trees, a creature as colorful as a jungle flower but burgeoning with teeth and hunger and death. A demon that seems to hunt people with a prophetic sense of final destiny.

But in the Cloudcrystal Skyfields, jiraskars are taken as hatchlings by some abhuman tribes and trained to the command of those wielding a yellow whip. Jiraskars have an innate ability to tap into the datasphere and this ability, along with their affinity for crystals, allows these abhumans to find special crystals that serve as potent foci for "magical power."

In some Pytharon cities, jiraskars are hunted like big game. They are prized for the sport they offer to those willing to enter the regions where the creatures roam and come back with trophies. But in addition to a mounted jiraskar head, the meat is also salvaged, because it's believed that eating a jiraskar steak adds a year to your life.

In other Pytharon cities, jiraskars are taken as hatchlings and trained to fight, sometimes to the death, as entertainment. Bets are common, and the amounts won or lost can be immense, especially when a favorite jiraskar enters the ring. Such fights also usually include a human trainer who either rides the jiraskar or runs around the ring. It's against the rules to specifically urge one's jiraskar to target an opponent's trainer, but accidents happen. Even if one jiraskar is disqualified because it ate the opposing trainer, side bets covering that contingency probably ensure that those backing the disqualified beast are made whole.

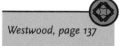

Westwood, page 137

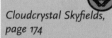

Cloudcrystal Skyfields, page 174

Datasphere, page 12

OTHER CREATURES

Analogs to birds, squirrels, midges, deer, cattle, and all the natural creatures of our current time exist a billion years in the future. But they're different. As a GM, you may want to add color to your presentation of a new area the player characters just discovered by describing the surrounding wildlife. If so, you can use this table to quickly generate weird attributes that the "birds" in the trees have, or the "cattle" in the field beyond the installation possess. Alternatively, if you're creating a new creature, you can roll on this table a few times for inspiration.

Roll	Attribute
1	Silvery threads pulse through this creature's body.
2	This creature's cube-shaped head floats unconnected over its body.
3	Instead of feet, this creature has slippery tendrils that allow it to skate along the ground.
4	Winglike frills allow this creature to hover in place, but they make a weird drumming noise.
5	This creature has no eyes, but it projects a thin line of red light from its forehead to sense its environment.
6	This creature absorbs all light that falls on it, making it look like a silhouette cut out of the air.
7	A fantastic network of thin ebony latticework sprouts from this creature's head like antlers or antennae.
8	Instead of teeth, this creature's mouth is filled with writhing worms that do the chewing and digesting.
9	Smoke (or some sort of vapor) constantly rises from this creature's mouth, eyes, ears, or other openings.
10	This creature's body glows pale white but blinks off when it is startled.
11	Three separate heads, each specialized for eating a different kind of prey, sprout from this creature.
12	Eyes as expressive as any human's dot this creature's carapace.
13	Hands as agile as any human's serve as this creature's feet.
14	This creature swells to twice its normal size every few rounds as it digests.
15	This creature always emits a wondrous smell.
16	When startled, this creature falls into dozens of subunits with tiny legs that scuttle away to hide.
17	Mushrooms, algae, and other growth cover this creature like a second skin.
18	This creature takes root like a tree for a few hours each day and can't move.
19	The scales covering this creature are full of delicate red lines that look like writing.
20	This creature enjoys a symbiotic relationship with large-winged insects that swarm to carry it through the air.
21	Ice forms around this creature, its breath steams, and its droppings are ice pellets.
22	This creature seems to be a collection of bubble-like spheres.
23	Red, twining tendrils cover this creature's head like a mane, one that might actually be a separate creature.
24	Crusted, bark-like growth partly covers this creature, which may be natural or may be indicative of disease.
25	Rainbow-like color patterns vividly refract light through and around this creature.
26	Blobs of liquid metal gather, move, and forage as if they were living creatures.
27	This creature sports a tail of treelike vines that each end in floating white orbs that glow and hum.
28	This creature periodically vomits up tiny, many-legged mites that burrow into the ground.
29	When the wind blows hard enough, this creature unfolds to five times its size and glides away.

30	Spines completely cover this creature, including its eyes, its hands, inside its mouth, and so on.
31	This creature is like a quadruped, but has only a single front leg and a single rear leg.
32	Spongy, somewhat translucent gel (red, blue, or green) makes up most of this creature's flesh.
33	Synth skin and blinking, glowing lights partly cover this creature.
34	Tiny insects constantly crawl over this creature's hide, forming a kind of self-repairing skin.
35	Branching black "stripes" cover this creature's pale skin, always moving and reforming.
36	This creature's call is a booming bass chime that brings forgotten memories to mind.
37	Legless and armless, this creature moves by a series of spastic jerks and convulsions.
38	Fires start around this creature, its breath smokes, and its droppings are red-hot coals.
39	Wingless, this flying creature moves through the sky by expelling rapid bursts of air.
40	Big-eyed and big-eared, this creature seems designed to be considered "cute" by most humans.
41	Red fluid constantly seeps from this creature's eyes. The fluid is sticky and acidic, attracting insects.
42	This creature's mouth makes up half its body. Inside the dark interior cavity, tiny gleams move.
43	This creature's horns end with flowerlike growths of red and yellow petals.
44	Multiple winglike membranes unfold from this creature's head, shedding heat or gathering light.
45	Fishlike creatures seem to swim within the translucent cavity of this creature's head.
46	Leaves form this creature's wings, which turn orange and drop off when the season changes.
47	Gel bodied, this creature leaves a residue that hardens into brittle crust.
48	Tiny spiderlike beings seem to animate this creature using thin threads covering its body.
49	Miniature automatons hover and flit around this creature.
50	Lightning sometimes strikes this creature, which it mostly absorbs without harm.
51	Once glimpsed, this creature fades from view for minutes at a time.
52	This creature has three sets of eyes, but only one set is open at a time.
53	Ragged tissue trails behind this creature like a noble woman's gown that's seen better days.
54	One of this creature's limbs ends in what looks like a metallic, broad-bladed cutting implement.
55	A beaked mouth on this creature's belly clicks and hums.
56	Triple jointed, this creature climbs on any surface with long limbs ending in weird claws.
57	This creature's presence seems to make using nano abilities and cyphers more difficult.
58	When this creature flees, it does so on tiny jets of purple flame, leaving trails of dark smoke.
59	This creature's carapace constantly swirls with different shades, as if liquid instead of solid.
60	Instead of eyes, this creature deploys vapor to sense its surroundings.
61	This green stalk growing from the ground crawls with tiny yellow maggots, each with a single eye.
62	The glass-like torso of this creature pulses with orange and green light.
63	This creature coughs and turns red when near cyphers and other objects of the numenera.
64	This creature swarms in patterns that create perfect circles, squares, and triangles.
65	Slime covering a dead creature animates and is revealed as a scavenger that is fast and fluid.
66	Sharp, bladelike bones serve as this creature's feet.
67	Resembling a bush, this creature shambles to a new location when disturbed.
68	Instead of a face, this creature has a flat surface studded with shins.
69	This creature seems to subsist on drit, and drit alone.
70	This creature retreats into a solid, egg-like shell when danger threatens.

71	Periodically, this creature turns itself inside out.
72	This large creature dangles the corpse of a dead human from its mouth as bait.
73	An eyeless head with a feeding mouth extends from this creature's stomach. Its main head has no mouth.
74	This whorled and crusted solid mass moves by extending leechlike legs from tiny holes in the base.
75	Water constantly drips from this creature, which is cold to the touch.
76	This creature dies when it leaves the flames for too long, becoming a solid, unmoving mass.
77	Sounds near this creature solidify into synth-like stones, which turn to sound again when the creature leaves.
78	When looked at, this creature puffs up its body to create a rough but credible mimic of the observer.
79	This creature's limbs move between it and other similar creatures, shared as needed and without harm.
80	Green fur covers this small creature, whose presence fills onlookers with a foreboding sense of doom.
81	A frill of ebony wings emerges from each side of this creature's head, fluttering almost like human hands.
82	Rocks and drit hover and swirl around this creature.
83	This creature's limbs split into smaller and smaller branches.
84	Circular mouths ringed with slowly swirling teeth are spotted around this creature's body.
85	A long neck doesn't end with a head but rather a flare of fernlike leaves with small eyes.
86	Elaborate nostrils shudder and breathe around the broad bulk of this creature's torso.
87	Each of these creatures seems to be made up of two or three smaller fused versions of the creature.
88	This creature can unfold the skin from its chest to reveal a mirrorlike surface.
89	Normally resembling oily, dripping black fluid, this creature can congeal and form into small slugs to escape.
90	This creature looks disturbingly like a human tongue that grows teeth on its surface like irregular scales.
91	Shadows near this creature always swirl and pulse to unheard melodies.
92	This creature's blood is a swarm of tiny automatons.
93	When this creature stands still, a tiny "crown" of pale light flickers over its head.
94	The bleating distress call this creature makes attracts other predators.
95	This creature constantly spins, so quickly that it's hard to tell what it actually looks like.
96	This creature seems to be made of light.
97	This creature "inflates" a hooplike arch on its back when threatened, then pulls itself into another dimension.
98	This tiny, hairless creature seems innocuous but is indestructible.
99	Beetle-like mandibles on this creature glow in response to the presence of bad memories.
00	This alabaster treelike creature can stand as if planted or move like a snake if startled.

PART 2:

CREATURES OF THE NINTH WORLD

UNDERSTANDING THE LISTINGS

Level: All creatures (and NPCs) have a level. The level determines the target number a PC must reach to attack or defend against the opponent. In each entry, the target number for the creature or NPC is listed in parentheses after its level. The target number is three times the level.

Description: Following the name of the creature or NPC is a general description of its appearance, nature, intelligence, or background.

Motive: This entry is a way to help the GM understand what a creature or NPC wants. Every creature or person wants something, even if it's just to be left alone.

Environment: This entry describes what part of the world the creature inhabits.

Health: A creature's target number is usually also its health, which is the amount of damage it can sustain before it is dead or incapacitated.

Damage Inflicted: Generally, when creatures hit in combat, they inflict their level in damage regardless of the form of attack. Some inflict more or less or have a special modifier to damage. Intelligent NPCs often use weapons, but this is more a flavor issue than a mechanical one. In other words, it doesn't matter if a level 3 abhuman uses a sword or claws—it deals the same damage if it hits.

Armor: This is the creature's Armor value. Sometimes the number represents physical armor, and other times it represents natural protection. This entry doesn't appear in the game stats if a creature has no Armor.

Movement: Movement determines how far the creature can move in a single turn.

Modifications: Use these default numbers when a creature's information says to use a different target number. For example, a level 4 creature might say "defends as level 5," which means PCs attacking it must reach a target number of 15 (for difficulty 5) instead of 12 (for difficulty 4). In special circumstances, some creatures have other modifications, but these are almost always specific to their level.

Combat: This entry gives advice on using the creature in combat, such as "This creature uses ambushes and hit-and-run tactics." At the end of the combat listing, you'll also find any special abilities, such as immunities, poisons, and healing skills. GMs should remember to be logical about a creature's reaction to a particular action or attack by a PC. For example, a mechanical creation is obviously immune to normal diseases, a character can't poison a being of energy (at least, not with a conventional poison), and so on.

Interaction: This entry gives advice on interacting with the creature.

Use: This entry gives the GM suggestions for how to use the creature in a game session.

Loot: This entry indicates what the PCs might gain if they take items from their fallen foes (or trade with or trick them). It doesn't appear in the game stats if the creature has no loot.

GM Intrusion: This entry suggests a way to use GM intrusion in an encounter. It's just one possible idea of many, and GMs are encouraged to come up with their own uses of the game mechanic.

Sometimes GM intrusions that you come up with on the fly based on the situation at hand will be better than a creature's suggested GM intrusion. Of course, that doesn't mean you couldn't use both ideas, if the combat lasts long enough.

GM intrusion, page 108

CREATURES BY LEVEL

*Creatures with asterisks appear in the *Numenera* corebook.
†Creatures with daggers appear in *The Ninth World Bestiary.*

LEVEL 1

Brendril	1
Caffa (larva)*	1
Chance moth†	1
Flesh pup†	1
Gazer†	1
Jacentwing	1
Laak*	1
Rapicaw	1
Stheed	1
Zayrn	1

LEVEL 2

Broken hound*	2
Caffa (adult)*	2
Chalik	2
Crystalvore	2
Dabirri†	2
Drebil†	2
Faradawk	2
Griffalo†	2
Heeldran	2
Hex stinger†	2
Margr*	2
Merkadian soldier†	2
Nacreon wind	2
Nausrak	2
Pallone*	2
Phaselost	2
Rubar*	2
Seskii*	2
Shanu†	2
Shivern†	2
Slurge†	2
Stratharian war moth*	2
Thuman*	2
Unagran†	2
Vape†	2
Ylaantiv†	2

LEVEL 3

Aneen*	3
Blood barm*	3
Calyptor†	3
Candescent sabon	3
Caprimag	3
Carnivorous color	3
Clicker	3
Coccitan†	3
Cypherid	3
Deiparon	3
Erulian†	3
Ghru	3
Glacier slime†	3
Golthiar†	3
Grey sampler†	3
Herder†	3
Ice weaver	3
Igothus	3
Jreet	3
Kalyptein crab†	3
Kaseyer	3
Keltonim	3
Killist†	3
Kissing fawn	3
Larus	3
Machine eater	3
Malvok	3
Mercurial wasp	3
Murden*	3

Nagaina defender†	3
Nalurus†	3
Nibovian child†	3
Nibovian companion†	3
Nibovian wife*	3
Octopus	3
Ocular & Tactile host†	3
Olion	3
Onrakas	3
Ort	3
Phasic	3
Pherotherm	3
Plasmar†	3
Rahenum courser†	3
Reconstructor	3
Rocira†	3
Sathosh*	3
Scutimorph*	3
Snow loper*	3
Spurn†	3
Steel spider*	3
Tetrahydra*	3
Therivar†	3
Torlethis companion	3
Ulenic	3
Weaponized meme†	3
Ylhath	3
Yovok*	3

LEVEL 4

Abykos*	4
Asomatis	4
Ateric	4
Avatrol†	4
Balikna†	4

Bithyran	4	Seskii tracer	4	Idyc	5
Blacktusk	4	Soshin	4	Imorphin gonoph	5
Cave qui†	4	Stalking shade	4	Imusten crawler	5
Chirog*	4	Steel angel	4	Jybril	5
Chronal feeder†	4	Syzygy ghoul†	4	Keeper	5
Culova*	4	Tachyron†	4	Lambrequin	5
Dal	4	Tarza	4	Latos adjunct	5
Decanted†	4	Terredel	4	Leradyt	5
Dread rider	4	Terror bird†	4	Llaric scorpion†	5
Ebon	4	Thexx	4	Lorub†	5
Entrope†	4	Thread walker	4	Magmid†	5
Ergovore hound†	4	Tonbrium hunter	4	Mesomeme*	5
Exigen	4	Trawl†	4	Mnethashi	5
Gleresisk	4	Umem	4	Moilt	5
Grush†	4	Urtilla	4	Morl†	5
Hungry pennon	4	Valma†	4	Mozck automaton	5
Iani	4	Vroaordun	4	Namnesis	5
Ithsyn*	4	Warder†	4	Neanic	5
Jesanthum†	4	Xaar†	4	Nibovian guide	5
Kanthid†	4	Xiomarche†	4	Nildir	5
Karestrel	4	Zandrel	4	Omath ranger	5
Klax	4			Orgulous†	5
Kroth	4	**LEVEL 5**		Peerless†	5
Lanmoro	4	Awakened nagaina sleeper†	5	Philethis*	5
Laurik-ca†	4	Blitzer†	5	Pygmy hapax†	5
Malork	4	Culova protector	5	Quar bastion	5
Mastigophore*	4	Cyclic raider	5	Quishamis†	5
Memora†	4	Datatar	5	Quover	5
Mlox†	4	Dazzlegad	5	Rahenum perceptor†	5
Navarac	4	Dimensional husk†	5	Relentless reaper†	5
Nerodrod	4	Disassembler*	5	Roummos	5
Nevajin*	4	Dream sallow†	5	Sarrak*	5
Nibovian domicile	4	Elaan	5	Shadow of the void	5
Nomyn	4	Ellnoica†	5	Silver orphan†	5
Odlark†	4	Erulian master†	5	Slicer beetle†	5
Oorgolian soldier*	4	Falling maw†	5	Slidikin†	5
Oorgolian tester	4	Flaw	5	Somenmal	5
Otolin	4	Flying elchin†	5	Sorg warbreaker	5
Pitystrian	4	Frilled baul†	5	Spiny scishan	5
Queb†	4	Ghost crab*	5	Stitcher	5
Raster*	4	Glauxim	5	Sweall	5
Ravage bear*	4	Golden cachinnate	5	Syzygid instructor	5
Rurtalian†	4	Hexon†	5	Tanglet	5
Scrivener†	4	Hontri†	5	Thusk	5

Varakith*	5	Shoguar	6	Redintegrad	8
Vesied	5	Symbate	6	Rhog†	8
Vuraneen	5	Travonis ul*	6	Tanaras	8
Engineered viral host: warrior host†	5	Unrast	6	Thundercrown	8
Xi-drake*	5	Voonex	6	Wharn	8
Yellow swarm*	5	Weld	6		
Zhev*	5	Xacorocax†	6		
		Xyst	6		

LEVEL 9

Eldmor	9
Marteling whale†	9
Pyth	9
Stellar weaver†	9
Versicolor truiskal	9

LEVEL 6

Abykos butcher	6
Accelerator†	6
Aliopter	6
Artifix	6
Astraphin monolith†	6
Banisther	6
Bellowheart†	6
Bloodfeast tick scion†	6
Cleoid	6
Corpuscular maw	6
Cragworm*	6
Cypher zealot	6
Decanted reaper	6
Effigy	6
Ember scion†	6
Encephalon†	6
Erodel shepherd	6
Erynth grask*	6
Etterick†	6
Ferno walker†	6
Fuser	6
Gevanic	6
Ishenizar†	6
Magathan†	6
Mimus	6
Morigo	6
Mujidavar	6
Nychthemeron†	6
Overlord automaton	6
Oxyuratl	6
Progenitor†	6
Rorathik†	6
Sasquand	6
Scavrow†	6
Shatarak	6

LEVEL 7

Arravelon	7
Callerail*	7
Cursed qui†	7
Dedimaskis†	7
Edacious destroyer†	7
Gaphelin	7
Gemorrn†	7
Incona	7
Ixobrychid	7
Jiraskar*	7
Jurulisk†	7
Kelursan	7
Lacaric courier	7
Minnern†	7
Multrolca	7
Neveri†	7
Null-cat	7
Psellis	7
Quotien†	7
Residuum	7
Rythcallocer	7
Skysmasher†	7
Sytor	7
Varadimos†	7
Vimruth	7

LEVEL 8

Dark fathom*	8
Dimensionworm	8
Earthshaker†	8
Kaorund	8
Kiprus, the†	8
Nagaina matron†	8
Puppet tree	8

LEVEL 10

Dread destroyer*	10
Latos†	10
Titanothaur†	10
Vow	10

RANDOM ENCOUNTER TABLES

RANDOM ENCOUNTER TABLES

Use these charts to randomly create encounters based on what the PCs are doing and where they're doing it.

EXPLORING THE RUINS

01–02	Abykos
03	Abykos butcher
04	Accelerator
05	Aeon Cavalier
06	Aliopter
07–08	Bandit
09	Bellowheart
10	Bithyran
11	Candescent sabon
12	Chalik
13	Chance moth
14	Chirog
15–16	Clicker
16	Coccitan
18	Cypher zealot
19–20	Cypherid
21	Dark fathom
22	Datatar
23	Decanted reaper
24	Dream sallow
25–26	Erodel shepherd
27	Erulian
28–29	Erynth grask
30	Exigen
31–32	Explorer
33	Faradawk
34–35	Flying elchin
36	Fuser
37–38	Gazer
39	Gevanic
40	Iani
41–42	Ishenizar
43	Ithsyn
44	Jacentwing
45	Kanthid
46	Keltonim
47	Lambrequin
48	Lanmoro
49	Latos adjunct
50–51	Margr
52	Mastigophore
53	Merkadian soldier
54	Null-cat
55	Nychthemeron
56	Odlark
57–58	Oorgolian soldier
59	Ort
60	Otolin
61–62	Overlord automaton
63–64	Philethis
65–66	Pitystrian
67–68	Psellis
69	Pyth
70–71	Quotien
72	Reconstructor
73–74	Rubar
75	Rurtalian
76–77	Sarrak
78	Sathosh
79–80	Spurn
81	Steel angel
82	Steel spider
83–84	Stitcher
85–86	Stratharian war moth
87	Symbate
88	Tanaras
89	Thusk
90–91	Travonis ul
92	Trawl
93	Ulenic
94	Voonex
95–96	Weld
97	Xacorocax
98	Xyst
99	Yellow swarm
00	Yovok

DELVING DEEP UNDERGROUND

01–03	Caffa
04–06	Cave qui
07–09	Coccitan
10–12	Crystalvore
13	Dark fathom
14–16	Entrope
17–19	Erynth grask
20–22	Etterick
23–25	Explorer
26–28	Gaphelin
29–30	Grush
31–32	Hungry pennon
33–34	Imusten crawler
35–37	Magmid
38–40	Malvok
41–43	Nagaina
44–46	Nausrak
47	Odlark
48–50	Onrakas
51–53	Phasic
54–55	Philethis
56–57	Quar bastion
58–59	Rapicaw
60–62	Ravage bear
63–65	Redintegrad
66–68	Sarrak
69–71	Sathosh
72–74	Slicer beetle
75–77	Somenmal
78–80	Stalking shade
81–83	Steel spider
84	Stellar weaver
85–87	Syzygy ghoul
88–90	Varakith
91–93	Vuraneen
94–96	Weld
97–00	Yovok

WANDERING THROUGH THE WOODS (OR JUNGLE)

01–02	Asomatis
03–04	Balikna
05–06	Bandit
07–08	Bloodfeast tick
09–10	Brendril
11–12	Callerail
13–14	Caprimag
15–16	Culova
17–18	Culova protector
19–20	Deiparon
21–22	Dream sallow
23	Earthshaker
24–25	Edacious destroyer
26–27	Encephalon
28–30	Elaan

31–33	Golden cachinnate
34–35	Golthiar
36–38	Jasmeris
39–40	Jesanthum
41–43	Jiraskar
44–45	Kissing fawn
46	Lacaric courier
47–48	Laurik-ca
49–50	Leradyt
51–53	Llaric scorpion
54–55	Murden
56–57	Navarac
58–59	Olion
60–62	Pallone
63–65	Philethis
66	Puppet tree
67	Queb
68–70	Quover
71–72	Ravage bear
73	Released, the
74–75	Scutimorph
76–77	Seskii
78–80	Slicer beetle
81–82	Steel spider
83–84	Stheed
85–86	Tarza
87–89	The Hex
90–91	Travonis ul
92–93	Vape
94–95	Vuraneen
96–98	Xiomarche
99–00	Ylaantiv

EXISTING IN THE FRINGES OF CIVILIZATION

01–02	Aeon Priest
03–04	Arch-nano
05–06	Balikna
07–08	Bandit
09–10	Blacktusk
11	Chance moth
12	Clicker
13	Cyclic raider
14–15	Culova protector
16–17	Deadly warrior
18–19	Decanted
20–21	Drebil
22–23	Flesh pup
24–25	Glauxim
26–27	Grush
28–30	Hollow glaive
31–33	Idyc
34–35	Imusten crawler
36–38	Jreet
39–40	Kaseyer
41–43	Keeper

44–45	Kelursan
46–47	Laak
48	Lacaric courier
49–50	Larus
51–53	Leradyt
54–55	Magathan
56–57	Malork
58–59	Mnethashi
60–62	Murden
63–64	Nagaina
65	Nacreon wind
66–67	Nalurus
68–69	Nano
70–71	Nevajin
72	Nibovian child
73	Nibovian companion
74	Nibovian guide
75	Nibovian wife
76–77	Nomyn
78	Null-cat
79	Omath ranger
80	Oorgolian tester
81	Phaselost
82	Philethis
83	Puppet tree
84	Quar bastion
85–86	Released, the
87	Rubar
88	Rythcallocer
89	Scuttling metheglin
90	Shivern
91	Slidikin
92–93	Syzygid instructor
94–95	Thundercrown
96–98	Town guard
99–00	Weaponized meme

TREKKING ACROSS THE PLAINS OR DESERT

01–02	Aneen
03–04	Asomatis
05–06	Avatrol
07–08	Balikna
09–10	Bandit
11–12	Banisther
13–15	Broken hound
16–17	Caffa
18–19	Calyptor
20–21	Caprimag
22–23	Chirog
24	Cragworm
25	Dazzlegad
26–27	Dedimaskis
28–30	Dimensionworm
31–33	Dread destroyer
34–35	Dread rider

36–38	Ellnoica
39–40	Encephalon
41–43	Ferno walker
44–45	Frilled baul
46–48	Ghru
49–50	Gleresisk
51–53	Griffalo
54–56	Herder
57–59	Igothus
60–62	Ithsyn
63–65	Jreet
66–67	Killist
68	Lacaric courier
69	Margr
70	Mazocacoth
71	Nomyn
72	Null-cat
73	Oxyuratl
74–75	Philethis
76–77	Quover
78	Quar bastion
79	Rahenum
80–81	Rorathik
82–83	Sarrak
84–85	Scavrow
86	Scuttling metheglin
87	Slurge
88–89	Sytor
90–91	Terredel
92–93	Terror bird
94–95	Tetrahydra
96–97	Thundercrown
98–00	Varakith

VENTURING CLOSE TO (OR UNDER) WATER

01–02	Blood barm
03–05	Cleoid
06–08	Ebon
9–11	Ithsyn
12–13	Jiraskar
14–16	Jybril
17–19	Kaorund
20–22	Karestrel
23–25	Killist
26–28	Kroth
29–31	Laak
32–34	Larus
35–37	Llaric scorpion
38–40	Lorub
41–43	Mercurial wasp
44–46	Mesomeme
47–48	Morigo
49–50	Morl
51–52	Murden
53–54	Nacreon wind

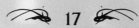

55–56	Nausrak
57–59	Octopus
60–62	Omath ranger
63–65	Philethis
66–68	Raster
69–70	Rythcallocer
71–72	Sasquand
73–74	Sathosh
75–76	Shoguar
77–78	Spiny scishan
79–80	Stratharian war moth
81–82	Tetrahydra
83–84	Travonis ul
85	Unrast
86–87	Urtilla
88–89	Vimruth
90–91	Vroaordun
92–93	Xi-drake
94–95	Xiomarche
96–97	Yellow swarm
98	Ylaantiv
99–00	Yovok

FINDING TROUBLE IN TOWN

01–03	Aeon Cavalier
04–06	Aeon Priest
07	Arch-nano
08	Blitzer
09–10	Candescent sabon
11–12	Cyclic raider
13	Deadly warrior
14	Decanted reaper
15–16	Effigy
17–19	Elaan
20–22	Flaw
23–25	Fuser
26–28	Glauxim
29–31	Haneek
32	Heeldran
33	Hungry pennon
34–35	Imorphin gonoph
36	Kaseyer
37	Klax
38	Lambrequin
39–40	Lanmoro
41–43	Malvok
44–46	Memora
47–48	Mimus
49–50	Mlox
51–53	Namnesis
54–56	Nano
57–59	Neanic
60–62	Nerodrod
63–65	Nibovian domicile
66–68	Nibovian guide

69–71	Overlord automaton
72–74	Philethis
75–76	Poisoner
77–78	Released, the
79–80	Scrivener
81–83	Seskii tracer
84	Seskii
85–86	Slidikin
87–88	Soshin
89–91	Thuman
92–93	Torlethis companion
94–95	Town guard
96–97	Warder
98	Xi-drake
99–00	Zayrn

WANDERING IN THE MOUNTAINS

01–02	Astraphin monolith
03–04	Callerail
05–06	Calyptor
07–08	Chirog
09–10	Cragworm
11–12	Ember scion
13–15	Ergovore hound
16–17	Erynth grask
18–19	Flying elchin
20–21	Hontri
22–23	Ice weaver
24–25	Kanthid
26–27	Kelursan
28–29	Killist
30–31	Lacaric courier
32–33	Latos
34–35	Latos adjunct
36–37	Margr
38	Mazocacoth
39–40	Multrolca
41–43	Nevajin
44–45	Orgulous
46–48	Philethis
49–50	Plasmar
51–53	Psellis
54–56	Pygmy hapax
57–59	Rapicaw
60–63	Ravage bear
64–65	Roummos
66–67	Rubar
68–69	Sarrak
70–71	Sathosh
72–73	Scavrow
74–75	Skysmasher
76–77	Snow loper
78–79	Somenmal
80–81	Steel spider

82–83	Sweall
84–85	Tanaras
86–87	Tetrahydra
88–90	The Hex
91–93	Umem
94–96	Vesied
97–98	Yovok
99–00	Zandrel

EXPLORING THE NIGHT

01–02	Aeon Priest
03–04	Aliopter
05–06	Arravelon
07–10	Artifix
11–12	Bithyran
13–15	Decanted
16–17	Ergovore hound
18–20	Gevanic
21–25	Ghru
26–27	Ice weaver
28–30	Incona
31	Ishenizar
32–33	Klax
34	Lacaric courier
35	Latos
36–37	Machine eater
38–39	Malork
40–42	Mozck automaton
43–45	Murden
46–48	Mujidavar
49–51	Navarac
52–56	Oorgolian soldier
57–59	Oorgolian tester
60–64	Otolin
65–68	Peerless
69–72	Philethis
73–76	Pyth
77–78	Quotien
79–80	Redintegrad
81–82	Sorg warbreaker
83–84	Shadow of the void
85–87	Slidikin
88–89	Symbate
90–91	Terredel
92–93	Thusk
94–96	Vimruth
97	Wharn
98	Xyst
99–00	Ylhath

EXPLORING OTHER DIMENSIONS

01–02	Abykos
03–05	Abykos butcher
06–08	Arravelon
09–11	Artifix
12–14	Banisther
15–17	Carnivorous color
18	Corpuscular maw
19	Clicker
20	Cyclic raider
21	Deiparon
22–23	Dimensional husk
24–25	Dimensionworm
26–27	Elaan
28–30	Eldmor
31–33	Flaw
34–35	Hollow glaive
36	Jacentwing
37	Jurulisk
38–39	Incona
40	Lacaric courier
41–42	Mimus
43–45	Namnesis
46–48	Neanic
49–51	Nibovian child
52–54	Nibovian companion
55–57	Nibovian domicile
58–60	Nibovian guide
61–63	Nibovian wife
64–67	Nildir
68–71	Ort
72–74	Phaselost
75–77	Pherotherm
78–80	Philethis
81–83	Seskii tracer
84–85	Shatarak
86–87	Shoguar
88–89	Stalking shade
90	Stellar weaver
91–93	Thexx
94–95	Thread walker
96	Tonbrium hunter
97	Ulenic
98	Varadimos
99	Versicolor truiskal
00	Voonex

UNCOVERING AN AREA WHERE NO LIVING THING SHOULD BE

01–02	Abykos
03–04	Accelerator
05–06	Banisther
07–08	Chance moth

09–10	Cypherid
11–12	Dal
13–15	Dark fathom
16–17	Dedimaskis
18–19	Dimensional husk
20–21	Disassembler
22–23	Effigy
24–25	Ellnoica
26–27	Ergovore hound
28–30	Erulian
31–33	Etterick
34–35	Falling maw
36–38	Faradawk
39–40	Gazer
41–42	Grey sampler
43	Imorphin gonoph
44–45	Jurulisk
46–48	Kalyptein crab
49–50	Kissing fawn
51	Lacaric courier
52–53	Mastigophore
54–56	Minnern
57–59	Moilt
60–62	Nerodrod
63–65	Onrakas
66–67	Oorgolian soldier
68–70	Oorgolian tester
71–72	Peerless
73–74	Pherotherm
75–76	Philethis
77–78	Residuum
79	Shadow of the void
80–81	Sweall
82–83	Syzygid instructor
84–85	Therivar
86–87	Travonis ul
88–89	Umem
90–91	Varadimos
92	Vow
93–94	Warder
95	Xaar
96	Xacorocax
97–98	Yellow swarm
99–00	Ylhath

INFILTRATING THE FORTRESS

01	Aeon Cavalier
02–04	Arch-nano
05–08	Ateric
09–12	Broken hound
13–16	Carnivorous color
17–20	Dark fathom
21–24	Deadly warrior
25–28	Dread rider

29–32	Effigy
33–36	Ergovore hound
37–40	Etterick
41–44	Grush
45–48	Heeldran
49–52	Iani
53–56	Jiraskar
57–60	Nano
61–64	Nibovian guide
65–68	Queb
69–72	Ravage bear
73–76	Shadow of the void
77–80	Slicer beetle
81–84	Steel angel
85–88	Steel spider
89–92	Town guard
93–96	Vape
97–00	Warlord

THE INDIVIDUAL'S MOUNT OR PET

01–04	Aneen
05–08	Avatrol
09–11	Broken hound
12–13	Deiparon
14–16	Ergovore hound
17–20	Ferno walker
21–24	Frilled baul
25–28	Griffalo
29–32	Hontri
33–36	Ithsyn
37–40	Jiraskar
41–43	Karestrel
44–45	Malork
46–48	Oxyuratl
49	Quar bastion
50–52	Queb
53–56	Raster
57–60	Ravage bear
61–64	Seskii
65	Scuttling metheglin
66–68	Shanu
69–72	Snow loper
73–76	Tachyron
77–80	Terror bird
81–84	Thuman
85–88	Thusk
89–90	Unrast
91–93	Urtilla
94–96	Warder
97–00	Xi-drake

CREATURES

Abykos, page 230

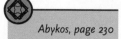

ABYKOS BUTCHER 6 (18)

A "ghost" that hungers for numenera is frightening. People know such a beast as an abykos. But even rarer and more dangerous is the related entity called an abykos butcher. An abykos butcher is a shadowy, hazy, vaguely humanoid shimmer in the air that carries a massive weapon (which might be a natural extension of one of its limbs). Normally incorporeal, it can be attacked only when it phases into reality.

An abykos butcher is more ravenous than a standard abykos. A butcher attacks any creature carrying powerful items of the numenera.

Motive: Hungers for energy from objects of the numenera

Environment: Abykos butchers can be found anywhere, usually alone but sometimes in the company of a regular abykos

Health: 26

Damage Inflicted: 6 points

Movement: Short

Combat: At the beginning or the end of its turn, an abykos butcher can choose to be insubstantial (phased) or solid. Once this decision is made, the creature can't change state again until its next turn. While phased, normal attacks can't hurt it, and it can move through solid matter except for force fields.

An abykos butcher's preferred method of attack is to turn solid at the beginning of its turn, then move up to a short distance as it whirls its weapon around it. Targets in its path must succeed on a Speed defense task or take damage and be knocked to the ground. Every target hit who carries at least one cypher or artifact of level 6 or higher must succeed on an Intellect defense task or one of those items (chosen by the GM) is drained of power and becomes useless. The abykos butcher gains 5 points of health per item drained when it does this, even if the increase puts it above its maximum health. Each item drained that contains transdimensional energy grants the butcher +1 to Armor for one minute while it's solid.

Interaction: Interacting with an abykos butcher is difficult. It does not speak or respond to the language of others, and telepathic communication yields no results, as if the creature does not exist. But an abykos butcher is not mindless; it can learn from its experiences and figure out creative solutions to problems.

Use: It's one thing to think you're dealing with an abykos. It's another encounter entirely when you realize that it's actually a bigger, more aggressive abykos butcher.

Loot: Often, devices of the numenera are near the location of an abykos.

GM Intrusion: The character who attacks the abykos butcher must succeed on an Intellect defense task or become phased. This allows the character to attack the butcher while the creature is also immaterial, but the PC can't interact with other solid matter until a means is found to reverse the process.

ALIOPTER   6 (18)

Like a horrific cloud of writhing, undulating tongues, alioptors sweep out of the cover of shadows to attack prey. These creatures fly by some unknown means of literally negating gravity in a precisely controlled manner. They are, in fact, colonies of many organisms fused together.

Motive: Hungers for flesh and seeks to reproduce

Environment: Prior-world ruins, especially those with spatial connection to the Gloaming

Health: 34

Damage Inflicted: 6 points

Armor: 1

Movement: Long (flies)

Modifications: Stealth as level 7; Speed defense as level 5 due to size.

Combat: Alioptors can attack all within immediate range with their barbed tongues. Creatures struck by this attack must immediately succeed on a Might defense task or be pulled into the mass of tongues and toothless mouths and held there. Victims held in this way suffer 6 points of damage each round if they cannot break free, although a new attempt is allowed each round. Held victims must also succeed on a Might defense task or be injected with alioptor larvae. The larvae live and grow beneath the victim's flesh for about a week, at which time they move to the tongue and cause it to swell. Eventually, the victim chokes, and each hour must succeed on a Might defense task or move one step down the damage track. After six hours, the victim's tongue ruptures, and tiny alioptors squirm out. The rupture moves the victim one step down the damage track. If the victim is dead, the young alioptors feed on the corpse before joining together into a single mass.

Once an alioptor injects larvae into a victim, it won't do so again for months, instead attacking prey simply to feed.

Interaction: The alioptor is a near-mindless predator that cannot be reasoned with.

Use: An intelligent native in a small town was killed, and a new alioptor emerged from the corpse. Now the residents are intent on finding and destroying the thing before it can claim another victim (and produce another alioptor).

The Gloaming is a vast artificial structure that exists far beyond the spiral of stars that contains Earth

The hideous effect of the alioptor larvae holds true for humans and humanoids. The process might take a different form in another creature

GM Intrusion: *The alioptor uses its control over gravity to affect the character. The alioptor floats slowly to the ground, but the PC is flung 15 feet (5 m) into the air and crashes down, suffering 3 points of damage unless they grab hold of something first or land gracefully (a Speed-based roll either way).*

ARRAVELON 7 (21)

That distant point of red light might be the top of some distant tower or beacon fire. Perhaps it's a falling star, or a craft fashioned of devices left from a dead civilization still flitting across the void. Or, if it continues to grow until it's a blazing point of scarlet fury several feet across, it might be an arravelon come to consume all your tomorrows, sucking away every shred of your potential until your future narrows down to nothing.

Motive: Hungers for minds

Environment: Almost anywhere

Health: 33

Damage Inflicted: 5 points (ignores Armor)

Movement: Long when flying

Combat: An arravelon can attack one target within immediate range with dozens of crawling tendrils of intangible light. A character who fails an Intellect defense task suffers 5 points of Intellect damage (ignores Armor) and experiences an odd sense of narrowing possibilities. Each time the victim takes damage, the difficulty of its Intellect-based tasks increases by one step. This effect lasts until the arravelon is destroyed or one day has passed.

An arravelon is vulnerable to attacks that use transdimensional energy. If damaged by such an attack, the creature falters and takes no action for one round, after which it can act normally.

Interaction: Arravelons don't speak or respond to the language of others, and telepathic communication yields no results, as if the creature does not exist. But arravelons are not mindless; they can learn from experiences and figure out creative solutions to problems.

Use: An inactive arravelon (which appears to be a node of reddish crystal) has been set into the ring of a powerful personage. Every so often, the arravelon manifests, killing the current wearer, though usually not when anyone else can see. This has given the ring a reputation for being cursed.

An arravelon subsists on the subtle interaction a conscious creature has on reality itself by observing it. Whether or not a timeline diverges depends on the choices a conscious creature makes. Once an arravelon has fully fed on a victim, no consciousness remains

GM Intrusion: *Instead of narrowing the PC's future options by feeding on their probability, it floods the character with so much probability energy that the PC must succeed on an Intellect defense task or pass out for one minute—or until roused—from the overload.*

ARTIFIX   6 (18)

Few people have ever seen an *actual* artifix. They see instead the silvery, translucent mental projections an artifix creates to serve, defend, and talk with. An artifix can create these free-roaming ambassadors at need, or dissolve them. Many mistake an artifix's ambassadors for an actual artifix, because that's all visitors are normally allowed to see. In fact, an artifix is an ugly, fleshy mass with vestigial limbs, too many eyes, and a slack mouth given to drooling. But the mind in that unfortunate husk is advanced far beyond human, and is deeply absorbed in some grand project or cause to which it's already devoted centuries of effort.

Motive: Accomplish personal mission

Environment: Almost anywhere

Health: 24

Damage Inflicted: 4 points

Movement: Immediate

Modifications: Knowledge of the numenera as level 9

Combat: An artifix is always accompanied by at least four silvery translucent ambassadors. Usually the artifix remains hidden, possibly in a nearby cavity, but potentially within an opaque, silvery mental construct carried by another ambassador. Ambassadors are separate entities, but all of them serve and defend the artifix that created them.

An artifix can create a new ambassador or other level 4 object as an action, which costs it 1 point of health. It creates objects for specialized needs, such as a shielding wall, a bauble, a path or door where none was before, and so on. Essentially, it can create any shape that fits into a cube that is 10 feet by 10 feet (3 by 3 m), as long as the shape doesn't exceed level 4 and the artifix has a point of health to contribute. Newly created objects last until destroyed or until they are separated from the artifix by more than a short distance.

Interaction: An artifix normally doesn't speak directly to visitors, leaving that to its created ambassadors. Each ambassador enjoys a limited autonomy, but remains devoted to its creator. An ambassador might describe the project that it and its "siblings" are attempting to accomplish, if it senses that the characters can help.

Use: New waves of silvery warriors emerge from a structure to defend it from the PC's approach.

Artifix projects are usually grand. For instance, an artifix named Meshala has taken as its project the "maintenance and defense of the sun."

Artifix ambassador: *level 4*

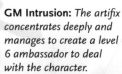

GM Intrusion: *The artifix concentrates deeply and manages to create a level 6 ambassador to deal with the character.*

ASOMATIS 4 (12)

Formless clouds of disconnected nanites until perturbed, asomatises are wayward entities whose origin is lost even to themselves. Some people believe they are minor avatars of the datasphere that were never reabsorbed. But as free-roaming clouds of potential, asomatises can solidify into specific shapes, including humans, animals, and dangerous creatures.

If its physical form is destroyed, an asomatis merely returns to formlessness and is unable to take that specific shape again, though it could reform in another body after a few days of rest.

Motive: Interaction
Environment: Almost anywhere, alone or in groups of three
Health: 15
Damage Inflicted: 5 points
Movement: Short
Modifications: Speed defense tasks as level 5 due to tactical connection to datasphere; tasks related to disguise and deception as level 6.
Combat: An asomatis uses whatever physical weapons are granted by its given shape, and may even gain +1 to Armor if the shape has it. For example, an asomatis who takes the shape of a glaive has a melee attack that inflicts 5 points of damage; as a ravage bear, it uses claws to inflict 5 points of damage. An asomatis doesn't gain special abilities from the forms it mimics, though it is able to evoke a mimicked creature's base physical abilities.

Regardless of its shape, an asomatis can access the datasphere to learn specific answers to tactical questions. This reduces the difficulty of its Speed defense tasks by one step.

If its form is destroyed, or if it decides to take a new form, it becomes a glowing red haze (which can be treated as an out-of-phase target with 1 point of health). Only transdimensional weapons can affect it in this form. The haze slinks off to recuperate if possible.

Interaction: An asomatis wants nothing more than to interact and attempts to ingratiate itself with strangers using a form that they are likely to find nonthreatening. The problem is that even though it pretends to have much knowledge, its connection to the datasphere is limited only to tactical information, which means asomatises lie constantly.

Use: An NPC is revealed as an asomatis when they are "killed."

GM Intrusion: *The asomatis mimics the character so successfully that the PC's friends have a difficult task ahead to tell them apart.*

ATERIC 4 (12)

Entities of information with an affinity for the numenera are called by many names, including spirits, ghost fabricators, and aterics. An ateric is nothing without a bit of mechanism to inhabit, but once it gains control of a cast-off bit of prior-world technology and is roused, an ateric can self-assemble over the course of a few rounds, becoming stronger and more dangerous as each second passes. Luckily, an ateric seems unable to hold this form for long, and whether defeated or not, it eventually falls into so much scattered junk. But in one of those objects, the core of the ateric remains, slumbering until an inexplicable call rouses it once more.

Motive: Destruction

Environment: Anywhere old devices are found

Health: 12

Damage Inflicted: Varies

Armor: 2

Movement: Short

Modifications: Attacks at an ever-escalating level.

Combat: A just-roused ateric has a rough but articulated form that it uses to batter and cut foes. Each subsequent round, a roused ateric draws inert mechanisms, drit, and even cyphers and artifacts carried by other creatures within short range into itself. As time passes, it grows stronger and more destructive—at least, up to a point, whereupon it falls back into so many scattered pieces of junk. Finding the "seed" device amid this junk is a difficulty 6 Intellect-based task.

An ateric's power increases according to the number of rounds it remains active, though never more than five contiguous rounds.

Round 1: Inflicts 3 points of damage; attacks as level 3

Round 2: Inflicts 4 points of damage; attacks as level 4; +3 health

Round 3: Inflicts 5 points of damage; attacks as level 5; +6 health

Round 4: Attacks twice; inflicts 6 points of damage; attacks as level 6; +12 health

Round 5: No additional change

Round 6: Spontaneous disassembly

Interaction: Aterics possess a kind of intelligence, but they are fractured, fragmented beings. Characters who can talk to machines might be able to keep an ateric from "spinning up" to become a threat and learn something valuable, but only for a short period.

Use: Among the cyphers collected from the ruin, one was actually an ateric that begins to self-assemble when activated.

Loot: An ateric that has undergone spontaneous disassembly leaves behind two or three cyphers; however, there's a chance that one of those cyphers is actually the ateric seed.

Some students of the numenera collect ancient devices that contain fragments of ateric consciousness in hopes of gaining control over the fabricated entity that self-assembles from that seed.

GM Intrusion: The character (or characters) must succeed on a Speed defense task or lose their cypher or artifact as it's pulled into the self-assembling ateric. The ateric gains a number of points of health equal to the level of the item.

BANISTHER 6 (18)

Banisthers may be guard creatures created by some as-yet-unrevealed species or entity who also inhabits the world of the incredibly small.

Banisthers don't hail from an alternate dimension, but rather a different scale. Normally part of the teeming flora and fauna that resides in a drop of water, banisthers can scale themselves up to hunt in the alien realm of the macroworld, where their abilities are difficult for regular creatures to contend with.

When scaled up, a gruesome banisther's total length easily exceeds 20 feet (6 m). Barbs and spines protrude from its tail. Its many feeding legs and voracious maw give most prey pause.

Motive: Hungers for flesh

Environment: Anywhere

Health: 22

Damage Inflicted: 6 points

Movement: Immediate; long when swimming

Modifications: Speed defense as level 5 due to size.

Combat: A banisther uses its feeding legs to make two attacks as a single action. In addition, if a victim fails a Might defense task, toxin on the legs inflicts an additional 2 points of Speed damage (ignores Armor) for three rounds.

A banisther can change scale while in combat, and may use an action scaling back down to less than a millimeter in length to escape prey that proves capable of defending itself. In addition, it can use its long tail to attack targets within 20 feet (6 m) to inflict the following effects:

Disruption: The foe must succeed on a Might defense task, or one of their arms or legs shrinks in scale to microscopic size, then returns to normal size. This distortion inflicts 8 points of damage (ignores Armor).

Body Theft: The foe must succeed on a Might defense task, or they are scaled down to less than a millimeter in height. To the victim, it might seem like they've been shunted to a bizarre dimension filled with writhing alien entities. The scale change reverts within a minute, unless the victim is killed while shrunk.

Interaction: Banisthers are simple predators.

Use: Ever since a local village started getting its water supply from a new well, they've been plagued by horrible creatures that randomly appear and disappear.

GM Intrusion: The character that is scaled down is threatened by a group of four level 4 creatures that have many legs and tendrils.

BITHYRAN 4 (12)

Bithyrans are perplexing creatures that probably originated far from the Ninth World. When they show up, they study a given area for its flora and fauna, and attempt to collect a representative sample of any intelligent species they find. Collected subjects may be gone for good, but other times they wake with little or no recollection of the experience save for bruises, missing digits or teeth, scabbed-over circular head wounds, and a gap of three or more days in their memory.

Bithyrans are difficult to see because their bodies are dark and elongated, and they have no joints, allowing them to fold into small spaces to await subjects. They have a series of eyes running along their limbs, and several manipulator hands. Devices of strange tech are worn as rings or piercings.

Motive: Knowledge

Environment: Anywhere intelligent creatures don't frequent and in the void of the night in groups of three or more

Health: 18

Damage Inflicted: 5 points

Movement: Short; short when climbing

Modifications: Knowledge-related tasks as level 7; stealth tasks as level 6.

Combat: Bithyrans can batter foes with their strong, boneless limbs, but they prefer to use items of technology that most always carry, including long-range ray emitters that can inflict damage or, with a flipped setting, induce deep sleep for an hour or more if the victim fails a Might defense task. Bithyrans prefer to cause as little damage as possible to potential subjects, so the sleep setting is used most often, except against automatons.

Bithyrans can increase their staying power by using cyphers that grant +4 to Armor for a few minutes. In case a specimen collection mission goes badly, at least one bithyran carries a cypher that creates a short-lived teleportation portal for instant transport to a distant and hidden base (which might be a spacecraft or a transdimensional redoubt).

Interaction: Bithyrans are always curious, and may negotiate if a means of communication can be opened. They use speech but speak at a frequency normally too high for humans to hear. Initial interactions are short because hidden bithyrans immediately leave when they realize they've been spotted. But they might come back.

Use: A family of farmers goes missing, and neighbors report seeing "slender, reaching shadows, like demon fingers" in the vicinity immediately before the disappearance.

Loot: A bithyran usually carries three or four cyphers.

GM Intrusion: *The character (or characters) wake after a long rest, only to realize that more than ten hours have passed. They all have strange marks and wounds, but no one remembers why. One of the characters (or an NPC) might even be missing. The only clue is a used transport cypher.*

BLACKTUSK 4 (12)

A cry that reverberates with what sounds like anguish typifies the hunting yowl of a distant pride of blacktusks. Those familiar with the noise know to find shelter, lest they become the pride's target.

A blacktusk is a catlike mammal over 7 feet (2 m) long with massive tusks. The creature's pelt is snow white, while its tusks are black as cloudy night in the Frozen South. A few populations of these savage hunters exist here and there across the world, but almost exclusively in areas of extreme cold. When humans venture into such areas, blacktusk prides might run them down as fresh food, or leave the newcomers alone and focus on prey they're more familiar with.

Hunters in lands far from the Steadfast are sometimes accompanied by trained blacktusks, which have been raised from kits to be companions in the hunt. Such blacktusks can be distinguished from their wild kin by the glowing cords of hemp-like material wrapped around their necks like collars.

Motive: Hunger or loyalty

Environment: Anywhere cold

Health: 12

Damage Inflicted: 5 points

Movement: Long

Modifications: Speed defense as level 6 due to quickness.

Combat: Blacktusks typically attack with their eponymous tusks, which inflict 5 points of damage, although they might also claw or pounce. If a blacktusk pounces, it is usually because the creature is attacking with surprise, or because it takes its first turn before its foe. A pounce attack inflicts normal damage but the victim must succeed on a Might defense task or be knocked down and pinned beneath the blacktusk until it can escape. Each round a victim remains pinned, the blacktusk savages it for 6 points of damage.

Blacktusks work together when hunting to increase their chances of bringing down prey, including more powerful creatures. Three or more blacktusks working in concert to attack the same target reduces the difficulty of one blacktusk's attack against the target by two steps.

Interaction: Wild blacktusks are vicious and cunning predators, but they are not suicidal, and if they have reason to believe their prey may be more than they can handle, they will break off an attack. If a lone blacktusk is encountered, especially one wearing a rope collar, it's likely a trained companion of some other creature, which is probably nearby.

Use: As encounters in cold wilds go, blacktusks are a great standby, especially if the PCs later encounter one as an NPC's "tame" companion.

GM Intrusion: The character injured by the blacktusk begins to bleed from the tusk wound, taking 2 points of damage each round (ignores Armor) until the PC spends an action bandaging the wound.

BRENDRIL   1 (3)

To many humans, these tiny, large-eyed, brown-furred creatures look adorable. But anyone who stumbles into a brendril burrow or who aggravates a brendril pack that's out scavenging learns that these creatures can be dangerously territorial. When a pack of brendril swarm over a target and hold tight, they're not giving affectionate hugs. Instead, they vibrate, spiking their internal temperature. A target in a pack's embrace is similarly heated rapidly, which kills and cooks most victims in short order.

When not killing predators, brendril packs encountered outside a burrowed mound housing the colony gather leaves, stems, berries, nuts, and similar foods to bring back to feed the colony as a whole.

Motive: Defense

Environment: Anywhere away from human or abhuman communities, usually in groups of ten or more

Health: 3

Damage Inflicted: 3 points

Armor: 5 points versus fire and heat

Movement: Short; immediate when burrowing

Modifications: Speed defense as level 3 due to small size.

Combat: A single brendril bites a foe and inflicts 1 point of damage from its fangs and 2 points of damage from a heat spike (a total of 3 points of damage).

When brendrils attack in a pack of three or more creatures, the pack acts as a single level 4 creature. A target hit by a pack is grabbed and embraced with strong, spindly arms. An embraced target can move, but the difficulty of all attack and movement-related tasks is increased by one step.

Escaping the embrace of a pack requires that the target succeed on a difficulty 5 Might-based task. Killing the embracing pack also works, but damage done to a brendril tightly holding a target is usually shared with the target. Each round a target remains in a pack embrace, it takes 5 points of damage from heat generated by the pack.

Interaction: Brendrils are not aggressive, and if given a wide berth, they will not treat characters as dangerous intruders.

Use: A caravan of merchants hires the PCs to serve as guards. Sometime during the trip, the PCs must deal with the threat of a roused brendril mound when some merchants stupidly smash one open.

Some hunters prize brendril furs, which provide wonderful insulation against cold (or heat).

GM Intrusion: *The heat from a brendril pack embrace cooks one of the character's cyphers, activating it, or activating it in an unexpected way.*

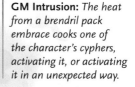

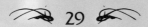

CANDESCENT SABON   3 (9)

"Given any seventeen integers, is there at least one subset of nine integers whose sum is divisible by 9? What are they?"

~a question posed by a candescent sabon

Rare and soughtafter, candescent sabons are thought of as oracles of truth, portals to the datasphere, teachers of magic and mystic philosophies, and—for those without the wit to understand the lessons offered—a dangerous and even deadly lure.

These entities are crystal orbs that usually glow with an enticing white light. While they are content to be carried around by someone who has claimed the creature as their own, a candescent sabon can float through the air like a disembodied star when it wishes.

Motive: Unpredictable

Environment: Prior-world ruins or in the possession of a student of the numenera

Health: 12

Damage Inflicted: 4 points

Armor: 2

Movement: Short when flying

Modifications: Knowledge of the numenera as level 8; Speed defense as level 4 due to size.

Combat: A candescent sabon can project a tiny energy orb at any creature within short range, inflicting 4 points of damage, if pressed to defend itself. However, it prefers to attack by establishing a mental link with a creature touching its surface. Each day—and after each conferral with the candescent sabon where the entity provides useful help—the entity poses one question, riddle, or puzzle of the user. The user must succeed on a difficulty 3 Intellect-based task to answer correctly. Every few days, the difficulty increases by one step. If the user gets a question wrong, the candescent sabon automatically inflicts 4 points of Intellect damage (ignores Armor) each round until the victim releases their grip, which requires a successful difficulty 5 Might-based task.

Interaction: Via telepathic communication enabled by touch, a candescent sabon offers all manner of diversions, including games set on imaginary boards, riddles, puzzles, and difficult questions. In return, it helps whoever has most recently claimed it with questions of their own. As long as the entity's questions (at least one per day) are answered correctly, it remains a helpful ally. But when a candescent sabon finds the intellectual limits of its latest user, it absorbs that creature's mind and moves on.

Use: An NPC working at cross purposes with the characters relies on a candescent sabon to get an edge on the PCs.

Loot: Most people would consider the entity to be loot in and of itself. However, a smashed candescent sabon might be salvaged for a cypher.

If a user takes a round to confer with a candescent sabon, the difficulty of all knowledge tasks, including those related to the numenera, is lowered by one step. But in return, the candescent sabon always requires the answer to a riddle of its own.

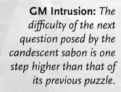

GM Intrusion: *The difficulty of the next question posed by the candescent sabon is one step higher than that of its previous puzzle.*

CAPRIMAG   3 (9)

Vaguely avian abhumans, caprimags can fly on feathered wings whose tips have a span of nearly 9 feet (3 m). They delight in the act of killing their prey as much as they do in consuming it. However, caprimags have learned that to survive they must be at least as crafty as the humans they often hunt. Having witnessed firsthand how humans supplement themselves with relics of the past to enhance their capabilities, caprimags have by and large endeavored to do the same.

Caprimags live in small flocks under a council of the three oldest, who've often lost the ability to fly due to infirmities, but whose minds are sharper than ever. The council is likely to have the lion's share of any items of the numenera gathered by younger flock members.

Motive: Hungers for flesh

Environment: Caprimags dwell in flocks of nine to twenty, usually in wooded areas or in hills abutting regions of open plains.

Health: 11

Damage Inflicted: 4 points

Movement: Short; long if flying (short if flying with a victim)

Modifications: Perception as level 5.

Combat: A caprimag attacks with talons and beak. To catch a foe and carry it away back to a nest, a caprimag dives from an aerial vantage from just beyond short range, moving about 100 feet (30 m) in a round, attempting to grab a victim near the midpoint of its path. A target must succeed on a Speed defense task or be jerked into the creature's taloned grip as it wings back into the sky.

A victim is held immobile by the caprimag's extra set of arms. The victim can take only purely mental actions or struggle to escape. Caprimags have a supremely unpleasant body odor that becomes overpowering to those held in their grip, which increases the difficulty of all tasks attempted by a victim by one step, including Might tasks made to escape. Of course, a victim who successfully escapes is probably looking at a fall of at least 50 feet (15 m).

Interaction: A few caprimags in any flock (including one or two elderly leaders) speak a human language in addition to their own language. Caprimags are hateful and angry, but not impossible to reason with, especially if items of the numenera are offered.

Use: A cache of sacred (or otherwise important) numenera was stolen by savage winged abhumans who flew off into the east with their loot.

Loot: One in every two caprimags carries a cypher, wearing it like a badge or amulet. Each leader has at least three cyphers and possibly an artifact.

GM Intrusion: *The caprimag uses a powerful cypher on the character, one that threatens to put the PC to sleep, render the PC suggestible, or otherwise turn the tide of an encounter to the caprimag's advantage.*

CARNIVOROUS COLOR 3 (9)

Ganim's white gloves and grey cloak turned blue. Everyone thought this was hilarious.
Until the blue ate Ganim.

~the writer Adoral

When creatures from bizarre dimensions leak into regular dimensions of space and time, the intruders often die immediately. Not so for creatures dubbed carnivorous colors.

A room with an eye-opening emerald source of illumination, a splash of brilliant scarlet on a wall, or even a set of familiar clothing that has undergone a spontaneous change in hue from grey to sapphire blue—all these might be signs of an infection by a carnivorous color.

Motive: Hungers for mental energy

Environment: Carnivorous colors can be found anywhere near spatial anomalies.

Health: 12

Damage Inflicted: 3 points

Movement: Short; immediate when flying

Modifications: Stealth tasks and attacks as level 5.

Combat: A carnivorous color attacks the mind of an intelligent creature within immediate range, inflicting 4 points of Intellect damage (ignores Armor).

Attacking a carnivorous color means attacking the object currently hosting the entity. Solid objects like walls might provide the color with a few points of Armor. A color rarely chooses to fight to the death, and may flee upward as a globe of illumination or seep along a wall or ceiling like flowing paint. If a host object (or patch of wall or ceiling) is destroyed, the color is disrupted and fades. Unless a weapon using extradimensional energy is used, the color isn't actually killed, just rendered inactive for several days.

When a color successfully eats the intelligence of a victim, the victim becomes darker as their color fades. The carnivorous color gains 3 points of health when it does this, even if the increase puts it above its maximum health.

Interaction: A carnivorous color does not speak or respond to the language of others, and telepathic communication yields no results, as if the creature does not exist. But a carnivorous color is not mindless; it can learn from its experiences and figure out creative solutions to problems.

GM Intrusion: *The character trying to use a cypher realizes it is a completely different color than the last time they stowed it—a brilliant green. Another carnivorous color attacks, this one hosted in the cypher.*

Use: PCs hear from a passing trade caravan about the sudden death of an entire village. The merchants found every living creature in town, including mounts and livestock, dead. The skin of every corpse was black as oil and nonreflective, absorbing light.

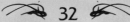

CHALIK   2 (6)

Chaliks are 1-foot (30 cm) long insects protected by elaborate yellow carapaces. They attack larger prey in small groups by sacrificing some of their number to catch and immobilize targets, allowing the remaining chaliks to freely attack and feed. They produce a surprisingly sticky secretion when killed or when they sacrifice themselves. They're found in warm wastelands, caverns, ruins, and sometimes run-down parts of human communities. Because chaliks can produce such a powerful bonding agent, craftspeople and others sometimes collect them for their fluid.

Motive: Hungers for flesh

Environment: Almost anywhere except cold areas in groups of ten or more

Health: 6

Damage Inflicted: 2 points

Armor: 1

Movement: Short; short when climbing

Modifications: Speed defense as level 4 due to size.

Combat: Chaliks swarm a foe and bite with their mandibles. A group of four or more chaliks can attack as a single level 4 creature that inflicts 5 points of damage. Alternatively, a single chalik can contract its abdomen and cause the glands inside to burst, resulting in a gush of sticky secretions from its mouth (and in that chalik's death). This is a level 4 attack that inflicts no damage, but a single targeted victim who fails a Speed defense task is covered in the secretion and immobilized (and unable to take actions other than attempt to break free) until it can escape. Attacks against a target immobilized by chalik secretions are two steps less difficult.

Chalik carapaces slough off their own secretions so they don't become stuck in the sticky material provided by their fellows.

Interaction: Chaliks are essentially insects, despite their size.

Use: A fight with an NPC becomes a lot more dangerous when the NPC knocks one of the characters into what turns out to be a chalik nest.

> **GM Intrusion:** *When the chalik is killed, it explodes. A character within immediate range is attacked as if by a chalik sacrificing itself to immobilize a target.*

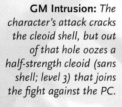

CLEOID 6 (18)

The spiral shell was partly translucent, revealing a mass of gelatinous slime wrapped along the tight interior path. Then a portion of it emerged, spreading spiny water wings, a whipping tail, and a hideous face whose gaze drank minds.

What cleoids call themselves is a term that is longer and more ominous, and one that can be conveyed only by telepathic contact. Victims hear this name each time they are psychically attacked by a cleoid, though most fail to appreciate the underlying meaning.

The legacy of a dead race survives concealed within "tainted" cyphers and artifacts as psychic seeds. Victims who use these devices are slowly transformed into massive monsters of slime and hate, partly enclosed in a protective shell. Dubbed "cleoids" by Ninth World explorers, these creatures want revenge for their racial eradication aeons earlier. Cleoids take that revenge on all living things.

Motive: Restoration of the cleoid race; revenge

Environment: Almost anywhere underwater

Health: 27

Damage Inflicted: 6 points

Armor: 2

Movement: Immediate; swim a short distance each round

Modifications: Speed defense as level 4 due to large size; tasks related to insight, detecting falsehoods, and knowledge related to psychic phenomena and psychic engineering as level 8.

Combat: A cleoid's main mode of attack is a psychic assault, which it can use against a single foe's mind within short range. The attack inflicts 4 points of Intellect damage (ignores Armor), and a victim must succeed on a second Intellect defense task or lose its next turn. A creature that would be killed by a cleoid instead falls into a 28-hour coma, during which time the victim is slowly transformed into another cleoid unless some kind of intervention occurs.

Interaction: Vastly intelligent and filled with hate for other living things, cleoids generally do not deign to communicate telepathically with other creatures.

Use: A strange plague afflicts a fishing community. Investigators find that those who succumb to its effects are slowly transformed and finally wake as cleoids.

Loot: A tainted cypher or two can usually be found near cleoid infestations. Carrying a tainted cypher for more than a few days risks the bearer becoming a host for a new cleoid.

GM Intrusion: The character's attack cracks the cleoid shell, but out of that hole oozes a half-strength cleoid (sans shell; level 3) that joins the fight against the PC.

CLICKER 3 (9)

These 9-foot (3 m) tall black, shadowy silhouettes are composed of focused sound. Predators from some other dimension, clickers feed upon any living creature that produces sound. They are blind, but they sense their environment and hunt prey by emitting rapid clicking noises—hence their name.

No one is certain where clickers originate from, but they seem to emerge at intervals through dimensional portals, swarm an area, and then vanish once everything living there has been consumed.

Motive: Hungers for flesh

Environment: Anywhere dimensional bleed occurs

Health: 12

Damage Inflicted: 4 points

Movement: Long

Modifications: Stealth as level 1 because of constant sound they produce; Speed defense as level 2 due to size.

Combat: Clickers are drawn to living creatures. A target must succeed on a difficulty 3 Speed defense task to avoid one's grasp or suffer 4 points of damage. The hit target then must succeed on a difficulty 5 Might defense task or be "swallowed." A creature so engulfed suffers 8 points of damage each round until it can escape.

Interaction: Clickers are easily mistaken for a simple predator. However, they are intelligent when encountered in groups of five or more, and negotiation is possible. But when they lose contact with other clickers, they devolve to a simple hunting existence.

Use: Clickers remain in areas with dimensional rifts, portals, or gates to their native dimension.

Loot: Only blood-soaked broken bones and shattered equipment remain from a clicker's past victims, though shins and some cyphers may survive the aural digestion process.

GM Intrusion: A destroyed clicker produces a sonic blast of nullifying noise that creates an area of silence a long distance across, negating all sound in the area for several hours or longer. Other clickers in the area are not affected, but instead act as if one level higher.

CORPUSCULAR MAW   6 (18)

A corpuscular maw consists of a small central core—the maw fragment itself— surrounded by knots of malleable flesh that can form into arms and tendrils. These "arms" serve as a means of locomotion as well as attack. The creature is covered in bony ridges, strange growths, and open tubes that spew foul smoke or volatile juices.

Each maw is a constituent creature spawned by a much vaster alien entity known as the Bloom. The Bloom is a leviathan-sized predator able to spawn doors into other dimensions at will within its mazelike interior. It subsists on the thoughts and actions (and sometimes the actual flesh) of those who enter it. Sometimes corpuscular maws are encountered within the tunnels that fracture the Bloom, but lately they've been encountered in distant locations and dimensions, sent by the Bloom for who knows what reason.

Motive: Follows the instructions of the Bloom, hungers for flesh

Environment: Almost anywhere

Health: 18

Damage Inflicted: 4 points

Movement: Long

Combat: Corpuscular maws mainly attack with their arms, which can extend a short distance, doing 4 points of damage to up to two foes on a single attack. Simultaneously, every other attack, they can release a cloud of fetid air that dazes the targets for one round or spray volatile acidic juices that do an additional 2 points of damage per target.

When a corpuscular maw is "killed," the flesh becomes unstable and bursts, causing a transdimensional wave that knocks all characters prone within short range.

Interaction: Characters who take two rounds to observe a corpuscular maw's behavior and feed it organic matter can attempt to interact with it (an Intellect task).

Use: Dimensionally stranded characters come across a corpuscular maw. If they can interact with it, they can perhaps get it to open its mouth wide and create a portal to another dimension. Whether that dimension is one the PCs want to go to is another matter.

More information about the Bloom can be found in Torment: Tides of Numenera—The Explorer's Guide.

GM Intrusion: *When the corpuscular maw is killed, every character caught in the transdimensional wave released by the creature must succeed on a Might defense task or be hurtled into a parallel dimension.*

CRYSTALVORE 2 (6)

These small transdimensional bugs—about 3 feet (1 m) tall—secrete a chemical that dissolves crystal. As part of their growth cycle, they break off a large chunk of natural or artificial crystal and partially hollow it out to serve as a shell. The majority of their bodies are hidden within the shell. What can be seen consists of spindly segmented legs and razor-sharp talons, claws, and mandibles.

Despite their name, crystalvores don't derive nourishment from crystal; they absorb ambient energy emanations through an unknown process. If such energy is not readily available, the creatures wander in search of food for a time, but if they fail to find any, they retract into their shells and enter a dormant state, appearing as normal crystals to the casual observer.

Over a crystalvore's lifespan, it will likely hollow out, wear, and eventually discard several crystal shells, each one larger than the last. As crystalvores are most often observed in the process of creating a new shell, the misconception that they "eat" crystals caught on and spread, hence their name.

Motive: Territory and defense

Environment: Anywhere near natural or artificial sources of crystal

Health: 6

Damage Inflicted: 2 points

Armor: 4

Movement: Short

Modification: Speed defense as level 4 due to size.

Combat: Crystalvores typically attack with their claws, but also have been known to spray their prey with a jet of the same fluid they use to hollow out their shells. This liquid is an almost universal solvent that does 3 points of damage (ignores Armor).

A mortally wounded crystalvore (with 1 point of health or less) will retract into its shell and spray its solvent all over the interior, weakening it in a multitude of places. The creature will then enter a unique biological state where its internal organs dissolve and a dangerous level of high-pressure gasses build up within the corpse, until finally releasing and igniting on contact with air. The resulting explosion shatters the creature's weakened shell, sending deadly shards in all directions. The process leaves no trace of the crystalvore, making a proper study of them difficult unless they can be captured alive.

Interaction: Crystalvores act like animals and are not intelligent. Territorial and aggressive, they ruthlessly attack any creatures that get too close to themselves or their domain.

Use: Crystalvores make impressive surprise attacks because they look like regular crystals when resting.

Crystalvores come from a dimension called the Ascension.

GM Intrusion: A crystalvore sprays its solvent in a wide jet, doing 3 points of damage to everyone in immediate range.

CULOVA PROTECTOR   5 (15)

Culova, page 236

Westwood, page 137

Most culovas are peaceful creatures that live in small groups in natural settings, leading simple lives. But that's not so for protectors, who sometimes serve as scouts, negotiators, infiltrators, and even assassins. A culova protector isn't trained; it's born. One out of every twenty or so culova eggs has the capacity to become a protector. However, culova groups that don't foresee near-term difficulties usually dispose of such eggs before they hatch, because protectors without a foe can become a liability to the group.

Culovas are spidery humanoids with eight spindly legs, a bulbous midsection, and a pair of humanlike arms with three fingers. Eight eyes adorn their heads like colored beads above disturbingly broad, toothy mouths. They move with astonishing quickness. Culova protectors can vary their coloration at will, allowing them to fade into the background.

Motive: Defense

Environment: Usually associated with other culova bands, particularly in the Westwood

Health: 25

Damage Inflicted: 6 points

Armor: 2

Movement: Long; short when climbing

Modifications: Speed defense as level 6 due to quickness; stealth and interaction tasks as level 7.

Combat: A culova protector prefers to attack from ambush, usually with two or three web traps deployed—as well as the backing of a couple of regular culova compatriots—to further increase its odds of success. A web trap is a level 5 sticky net that ensnares an unsuspecting victim, preventing them from taking any actions until they can escape. Attacking a victim in a web trap is two steps less difficult.

Culova protectors also rely on envenomed crossbows of their own making that inflict 6 points of damage plus 6 points of Speed damage (ignores Armor) for two rounds on those who fail a Might defense task.

In addition, protectors can spray venom from their mouths on all creatures within 10 feet (3 m). Victims must succeed on a Might defense task or take 6 points of Speed damage (ignores Armor).

Interaction: A culova protector can usually speak several languages, including the Truth. They are adept negotiators, and delight in crafting deals that improve the standing of their culova group. However, a protector is not above false dealing, especially when trying to lure those it judges as a threat to its people into a trap.

Loot: Culova protectors are more worldly than the average culova, and usually carry 2d10 shins, one or two cyphers, and their custom-made crossbows.

The Truth, page 133

GM Intrusion: *The web trap catching the character is more complex than it first seemed. In addition to preventing the PC from taking any actions except attempts to escape, it threatens to fling the character into a deep crevice, a fire, or something similar within two rounds.*

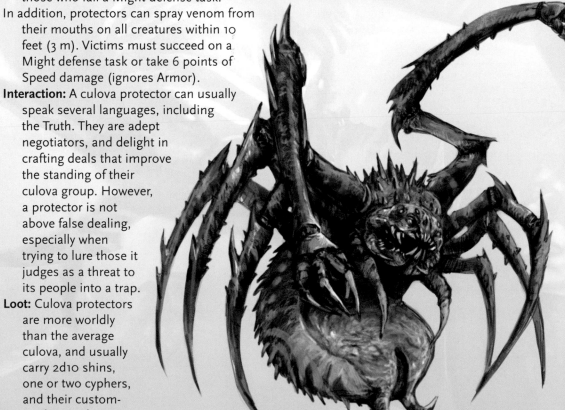

CYCLIC RAIDER   5 (15)

Cyclic raiders are humanoid automatons powered by sound. A flat, blank silver disc is displayed where their face should be. They appear at intervals that seem completely random, though some students of the numenera claim their schedule can be determined ahead of time with enough calculation. However, those who are too successful at discovering that secret tend to become the latest targets of the raiders.

Cyclic raiders usually appear suddenly, as if they'd stepped out of an invisible door. They disappear just as precipitously, exactly three minutes later, often with a captive or two.

Motive: Capture test subjects (usually humans)

Environment: Almost anywhere, alone or in groups of three

Health: 20

Damage Inflicted: 4 points

Movement: Short; long when jumping

Armor: 2

Modifications: Speed defense as level 6; knowledge of other worlds and galaxies as level 7.

Combat: Cyclic raiders use a device they call a Melu box to render human targets unconscious.

Raiders avoid direct engagement and are expert at dodging incoming attacks (reflected in their level 6 Speed defense). If forced to defend themselves, they fire a sound blast that inflicts 4 points of Intellect damage (ignores Armor) on a failed Intellect defense task.

In areas with ambient sound, these automatons require no sustenance and operate indefinitely. But in completely soundless areas, such as the void beyond the sky, they collapse and can be restored to function only when exposed to sound.

Interaction: Cyclic raiders enact a bizarre agenda. They ambush, incapacitate, and somehow transport humans to another world in the void of space for an unknown purpose. They speak several languages, which seem to be composed of voice recordings of various humans sewn together to make complete new sentences.

Use: The PCs arrive to consult with someone who has information or an item they want, but that person is being attacked by cyclic raiders.

Loot: A fallen cyclic raider can be salvaged for a couple of cyphers. Any group of raiders will probably have one Melu box.

> **GM Intrusion:** A defeated cyclic raider goes through sudden convulsions, its limbs shifting and locking into strange shapes as a second raider leaps on it. They both snap together to create a much larger level 7 creature.

MELU BOX (ARTIFACT)

Level: 1d6 + 3

Form: Small silver box

Effect: When activated, every living creature in short range that can hear must succeed on an Intellect defense task or fall unconscious. Unconscious creatures can attempt an Intellect task each round to rouse themselves.

Depletion: 1 in 1d10

CYPHERID 3 (9)

The clattering, scuttling sound of a single cypherid climbing through a hidden duct or channel is disquieting, but hearing a swarm approach is terrifying.

Cypherids are automatons that are essentially an animate accumulation of cyphers. Like vermin, they sometimes conglomerate in ruins. They flit, clamber, slide, or trundle along on limbs made of disparate devices, though there is an overall spiderlike body structure to the creature. A cypherid generally doesn't reach dimensions larger than a couple of feet (60 cm).

Like an insect, a cypherid seems driven by simple motives. In this case, it is to accumulate more cyphers to add to itself as older components get used up or burn out.

Motive: Defense, find cyphers to repair themselves and seed new cypherids

Environment: Usually in prior-world ruins, alone or in groups of two to five

Health: 9

Damage Inflicted: 3 points

Armor: 2

Movement: Short

Modifications: Speed defense as level 4 due to size; uses cyphers as if cyphers were level 5.

Combat: Cypherids can batter or stab foes with their limbs, but they prefer to try to pilfer a PC's cyphers. If one feels especially threatened, it uses a cypher-like function available to it. The cypher effect could be a ray emitter, a detonation, a gravity wave that holds the characters down, a phasing cypher that allows the cypherid to get away, and so on. Alternatively, the GM can use whatever method they normally use to generate random cyphers.

When a cypherid attacks a character carrying a cypher, the PC must succeed on an Intellect defense task or the cypherid snakes a glassy tendril into the character's equipment and comes away with a cypher chosen by the GM. Along with any other action it takes on its next turn, the cypherid can add the cypher to itself, which grants the creature 5 points of health even if this takes it over its normal maximum.

Interaction: Cypherids are not intelligent and do not communicate, though a few with cyphers that allow communication with the datasphere or similar abilities can gain intelligent behaviors and advanced motives for a time.

Use: The characters learn that a nearby ruin is supposed to be rich in cyphers. Upon arriving they find that it's true only in a way— the ruin is crawling with cypherids.

Loot: About three cyphers can be salvaged from a cypherid's body.

A swarm of cypherids can act as a single level 5 creature that inflicts 5 points of damage and creates level 7 cypher effects.

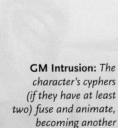

GM Intrusion: *The character's cyphers (if they have at least two) fuse and animate, becoming another cypherid.*

DAL 4 (12)

Dal are creatures native to a realm of just two dimensions (length and width, but not height). In our dimension they appear as complex, organic patterns scrawled on the wall or inscribed on the floor, at least until they move. Then they resemble flowing liquid—if liquid could run counter to gravity, under its own power, with surprising speed and agility.

Dal are transdimensional refugees, seeking to find the lost dimension from which they were cast out. Why that requires them to prey upon creatures from normal dimensions of space and time isn't clear.

Motive: Exploration, survival

Environment: Almost anywhere in groups of two to four

Health: 15

Damage Inflicted: 5 points

Movement: Short; able to fade into an alternate dimension up to once each hour as an action

Modifications: Knowledge of other dimensions as level 5; Speed defense as level 5 due to existing only in two dimensions.

Combat: A dal can race along a surface but also raise itself above the surface and use its thin body as a blade to attack a target. In addition, most dal can affect their surroundings by directly manipulating the fabric of spacetime, and can create one of the following effects.

Dissonance: A long-range sonic attack against a single foe.

Alienation: An immediate-range psychic attack against a single foe who takes Intellect damage (ignores Armor) and on a failed Might defense task loses their next turn.

Transfer: An immediate-range attack that transfers both the dal and its victim into an alternate dimension if the victim fails a second Intellect defense task. This alternate dimension might look exactly like the one just departed, except be empty of life. Victims phase back to their plane of origin after a few rounds.

Interaction: Dal easily pick up new languages, and they can create a buzzing dissonance in the air to mimic speech or move their two-dimensional bodies in such a way as to create symbols and even short phrases. If communication can be opened, they might negotiate for new transdimensional knowledge or a fresh food source.

Use: Strange signs and symbols appeared on the home of a local merchant, who hasn't been seen in a few days. The symbols have grown more complex over time, and some people suspect it is writing asking for aid. But it might just be a trap.

GM Intrusion: *The dal lifts completely off the wall or ground and spins itself like a deadly thin disc at the character, slicing through the air. On a failed Speed defense task, the PC takes 5 additional points of damage (10 points total).*

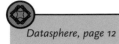

Datasphere, page 12

DATATAR 5 (15)

Nano powers, certain devices, and special areas allow people to tap into the all-pervasive datasphere to learn information or gain other assets. Additionally, people in the Ninth World experience "glimmers" that are strange, random glimpses of information or images that come from the datasphere. The datasphere sometimes relies on avatars known as datatars to accomplish these tasks. Sometimes a datatar aids the one who asked the question, had the glimmer, or tried to trigger some other service from the datasphere. Other times, a datatar views the intrusion as a malfunction that must be eliminated.

A datatar appears as an exotic, three-dimensional image of light, usually rapidly iterating through complex shapes and equations that draw the eye. It can affect matter by creating manipulative force fields.

Motive: Unpredictable

Environment: Almost anywhere

Health: 15

Damage Inflicted: 5 points

Movement: Short when flying

Modifications: Most knowledge tasks as level 9.

Combat: A datatar can be affected only by energy weapons or similar implements.

Datatars can discharge electromagnetic energy or a battering force field to attack a foe within long range.

They can also tune themselves to display a customized mind-infecting pattern at a foe within immediate range who fails an Intellect defense task. An affected foe stands entranced until they can escape the trance by succeeding on a difficulty 6 Intellect-based task.

Each round in which a victim remains entranced, knowledge is siphoned from the victim's mind, inflicting 2 points of Intellect damage (ignores Armor).

Composed of regenerating light, datatars regain health at 2 points per round as long as they have at least 1 point of health.

Interaction: A datatar can speak any language, including languages used by machines. Some datatars do not negotiate, though a few are more interested in exploration than castigation.

Use: When a creature uses an ability related to the datasphere, a datatar may appear.

An expert on the datasphere could probably figure out some way to engage a datatar on an esoteric level by attempting to alter its underlying instructions.

GM Intrusion: *The datatar visually imparts a concept so large and complex that a human mind can't hold it for long. The concept may provide the character with a necessary edge, but it also causes the PC to descend one step on the damage track.*

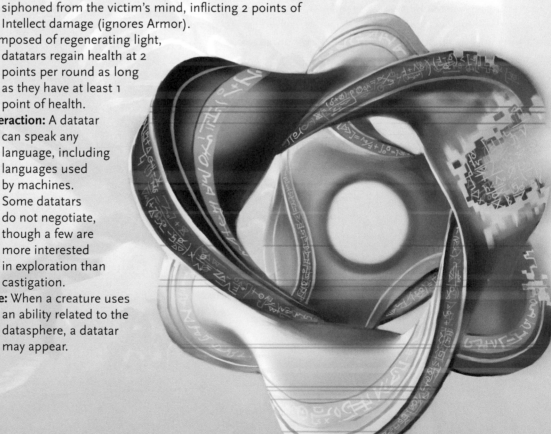

DAZZLEGAD 5 (15)

You can't mistake a dazzlegad, even one that is miles away. Though it's a large and somewhat clumsy-looking beast twice the size of a human, the mirrorlike organs on its face, head, and back can hide it within a pulse of light almost as intense as the sun. Looking at the dazzlegad when it's at its brightest risks an observer's eyes, leaving afterimages for minutes or even hours afterward.

Though it is chiefly concerned with hunting, eating plants and animals it can catch on the open plains and deserts it prefers, a dazzlegad is somewhat intelligent. When dazzlegads find caches of the numenera that can relay information, they somehow absorb that knowledge and replay it using light images. It's a little-known fact that a dazzlegad's cache of personally stored information sometimes reaches back through several iterations of the prior worlds.

Motive: Hungers for flesh

Environment: Plains or deserts

Health: 25

Damage Inflicted: 6 points

Armor: 2

Movement: Short

Modifications: Attacks and Speed defense as level 6 due to visual glare.

Combat: A dazzlegad can trample up to two foes next to each other. When it wishes, it can focus its light into a burning beam able to target a creature within long range, inflicting 6 points of damage. It can also accomplish other things with its ability to generate and shape light:

Blind one target within short range and all targets within immediate range for about a minute if they fail a Might defense task.

Create a convincing illusion of the arrival of a far more serious threat, such as a dimensionworm.

Beam a pulsing light display into the eyes of a target within short range, sending them into a seizure lasting a few rounds if they fail a Might defense task. This effect inflicts 3 points of Speed damage (ignores Armor).

Beam a disorienting light pulse that confuses a target within short range who fails an Intellect defense task, causing them to attack a random target next round.

Interaction: Characters who can generate light and use it to signal a dazzlegad might be able to open communications. The creature is willing to negotiate when it's not hungry, so providing it with something to eat is also useful. After that, it might work with the characters, leave them alone, or share a piece of visual information it has stored. A dazzlegad has total visual recall, and can recreate any scene it has witnessed or accessed via light communication.

Use: The PCs were looking for an old hermit who supposedly knows secrets of the prior worlds. Instead they stumble across a dazzlegad eating the hermit's body.

Dimensionworm, page 46

GM Intrusion: *The character struck by the dazzlegad's light is blinded. The PC can attempt a Might defense task once per day to shake off the effect.*

DECANTED REAPER 6 (18)

Decanted: *level 4; Armor 3; inflicts 5 points of damage; see page 34 of The Ninth World Bestiary for more information*

A frozen human head, held immobile in a frosted glass dome, serves as the controlling mind for a vicious automaton covered in synth armor and studded with sickle-like blades and energy sabers. The head is the controlling intelligence for the artificial body, purposefully selected and placed there based on an especially cruel and cunning streak by other frozen heads with prosthetic bodies. Which is saying something, since all the decanted are devious and lacking in empathy for normal humans. Decanted reapers are expected to defend regular decanted, and guard the places where decanted establish their colonies.

A city called Glass is peopled by several hundred decanted and a hundred times that number of glass containers, each holding a preserved human head of ancient vintage floating in a bath of air so cold that it's become liquid. More than a dozen decanted reapers wander Glass, but they're also often sent out on missions into the Ninth World in search of fresh heads.

Motive: Defend and do the bidding of normal decanted

Environment: Almost anywhere, alone or in the presence of two normal decanted

Health: 33

Damage Inflicted: 8 points

Armor: 3

Movement: Short; short when climbing; long when leaping

Modifications: Stealth as level 8 when using visual distortion field.

Combat: A decanted reaper often makes its initial attack from ambush by relying on a visual distortion field that renders it nearly invisible. The field collapses if the decanted reaper attacks or makes a long-range leap to enter combat. Targets that are surprised by the initial attack take 2 additional points of damage (for a total of 10 points).

GM Intrusion: *The PC's attack ruptures an internal conduit containing freezing fluid, which sprays into the character's eyes. They are blinded for several minutes if they fail a Might defense task.*

A reaper can use its claws and energy sabers to attack every creature within immediate range.

If it decides it wants a target's head, a decanted reaper uses an energy saber to attack just one target within immediate range. The damaged target must succeed on a Might defense task or descend one step on the damage track as the reaper attempts to sever its head The reaper keeps up this tactic on the chosen target until the target descends all three steps on the damage track and its cauterized head comes free. The reaper then "ingests" the liberated head and stores it in an interior chamber filled with liquid that's colder than ice for later processing.

Interaction: Most decanted reapers are vicious killers and defer to regular decanted. However, most know one or more human languages.

Use: A character is targeted by a decanted reaper who decides that it would like that PC's head.

Loot: The remains of a decanted reaper can be salvaged for 1d6 cyphers and possibly an oddity.

DEIPARON   3 (9)

"They say that a deiparon's glow is actually the eye of a god looking out, so be wary of what you do where a deiparon can see you.

~Belrem the jack

Ornery and vindictive, deiparons usually hunt alone unless caring for their young, in which case three to five of them travel together for several months. Deiparons are reptilian creatures with several legs equally good for running and climbing. Among other physical oddities, deiparons sport a glowing spherical energy orb in a concave hollow on their backs. The orb constantly discharges energy in flares and pulses. Most of the time, the discharge is small. But if roused, a deiparon can focus that energy against prey or use it in defense if attacked by more vicious predators.

Motive: Hungers for flesh

Environment: Woods and jungle, alone or in packs of three to five

Health: 12

Damage Inflicted: 4 points

Armor: 2

Movement: Short; short when climbing

Modifications: Perception tasks as level 6.

Combat: Deiparons pounce on prey when they attack, from the branches of overhanging trees if possible. However, a deiparon can also deal 6 points of damage from the energy orb on its back to a creature within short range. Each time they do so, they lose 1 point of health.

In rare instances, a deiparon uses its energy to trigger a transformation that grants it intelligence at least equal to a human's, as well as the abilities of a level 6 creature. This effect usually lasts for no more than a minute. The deiparon uses its temporary intelligence to defray a conflict, unless it sees a way to defeat foes through trickery or some other stratagem.

Interaction: Deiparons have animal-level intelligence most of the time. In rare instances, they can transform to become incredibly intelligent and gain the ability to speak in most languages, during which time negotiation may be possible.

Use: A local lord keeps a "pet" deiparon in her menagerie. She swears that sometimes it talks and knows the answer to an important secret. But the beast never seems to do so in front of others.

GM Intrusion: *the deiparon transforms into an intelligent level 6 version of itself and uses its newfound mental capacity to trick, trap, or get away from the PCs.*

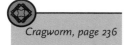
Cragworm, page 236

DIMENSIONWORM   8 (24)

When a terrible, mournful howl is heard reverberating from nowhere, the source might be a dimensionworm tunneling through layers of reality looking to feed. Possibly related to the cragworm, a dimensionworm is a spiny serpent that can grow up to 50 feet (15 m) long. Dwelling in abandoned parallel dimensions or possibly even in the "walls" separating alternate planes, it preys on whatever it can find.

When a dimensionworm enters a new dimension, it usually inserts only part of its long body, just enough to catch and consume prey.

Like their purely terrestrial cousins, dimensionworms have the intelligence of an animal and the outlook of a predator.

Motive: Hungers for flesh
Environment: Anywhere dimensional fabric is weak
Health: 56
Damage Inflicted: 10 points
Armor: 2
Movement: Short
Modifications: Speed defense as level 5 due to size; resists trickery as level 3.
Combat: A dimensionworm hides in a parallel dimension, but it can see through the walls of the worlds to find new prey. Even while dimensionally separated from prey, its howls possess a transdimensional resonance able to paralyze a target and anyone within immediate range of the target. Victims who fail Intellect defense tasks are paralyzed until they can mentally shake off the effect.

When the anterior portion of a dimensionworm appears from what seems to be empty space to attack, its massive blunt head batters the target and all creatures within short range of the target. The target, however, must succeed on a Might defense task from the envenomed bite or move one step down the damage track.

Because a dimensionworm normally extends just a portion of its length into another plane, prey never see the worm's entire length unless they're pulled out of their home dimension and into the worm's. A dimensionworm uses its ability to transcend planes defensively as well as offensively, and retreats back from whence it came if combat is going poorly for it.

Once every few rounds, a dimensionworm can burrow through dimensional walls as part of its movement. The hole created closes up a few rounds after it is no longer being used by the worm.

Interaction: Dimensionworms can't be reasoned with. They can be intimidated or tricked, but the latter is far easier than the former. They resist being tricked as level 3 and are particularly easy to fool if food is involved.

Use: Dimensionworm teeth seem to have a dimensional resonance useful for those who want to try to transcend their own reality. A few nanos who work for the University of Doors offer contracts to those who can supply such teeth.

GM Intrusion: *The dimensionworm pulls a character who fails a Speed defense task to an abandoned parallel plane so it can dine on its prey without interference.*

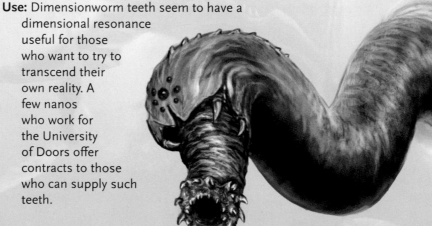

DREAD RIDER 4 (12)

Giant war machines known as **dread destroyers** have a well-deserved reputation for being the most horrific—and probably the very last—thing a Ninth Worlder will ever see. Heavy, metallic, and monstrous, these ancient automatons carry enough weaponry to level any three cities.

But almost as horrific as the destroyer is the so-called dread rider, who sometimes appears in the weeks and days before a dread destroyer makes its thunderous presence known, like a herald of doom.

Motive: Defense

Environment: Anywhere near a dread destroyer

Health: 15

Damage Inflicted: 6 points

Armor: 3

Movement: Short

Modifications: Might defense tasks as level 6.

Combat: A dread rider can make a single attack with an electricity-infused weapon for 6 points of damage (4 points from the blade and 2 points from the electricity). The 2 points of electricity damage always ignore Armor.

A dread rider can use several special abilities, including the following.

Lightning Storm: The dread rider becomes immune to electricity even as it sheets over their metallic bodies. Anyone within immediate range of a dread rider takes 1 point of damage each round, and the dread rider inflicts an additional 2 points of damage from electricity each round.

Recall: The dread rider immediately teleports to the nearest dread destroyer, which could be many hundreds of miles away.

Summon: The dread rider summons a dread destroyer, which usually arrives within a few hours. Most of the time, a rider won't do this, even if it's in personal danger, unless it feels some greater purpose could be achieved.

Death Trigger: If a dread rider is killed, a dread destroyer is summoned.

Interaction: Most dread riders have human brains and were only recently "harvested" by a dread destroyer to serve as an agent. A dread rider remembers some of its past life, but it is committed to searching the world for "enemies," even though who or what those enemies are isn't really clear. Individual dread riders can also be motivated by fear, greed, grief, or revenge, and they negotiate accordingly.

Use: An angry dread rider has appeared in the city and must be dealt with carefully to avoid triggering the appearance of a dread destroyer. The first task is to determine what the dread rider wants.

Loot: The remains of a dread rider can be salvaged for 1d20 shins, one or two additional cyphers, and an oddity.

Dread destroyer, page 239

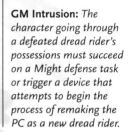

GM Intrusion: *The character going through a defeated dread rider's possessions must succeed on a Might defense task or trigger a device that attempts to begin the process of remaking the PC as a new dread rider.*

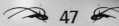

EBON 4 (12)

Like the shadow of a shadow, an ebon slips through the water soundlessly, noiselessly, and nearly imperceptibly. Streamlined and sleek, they are designed to be the perfect hunters. They can move from a still float to a prey-dive in less than a second, thanks to their elongated, finned arms and strong tails. They hunt and eat almost constantly, as they require large amounts of food, particularly fat, to fuel their revving metabolisms.

Ebons fight among themselves constantly for power, position, and the best bits of food. They often start eating their prey before it's completely dead to ensure that they get the choice bits before another member of their pack swoops in for a steal. Additionally, the sooner they eat after an attack, the more of their own poison they ingest, which temporarily increases their toxicity.

Motive: Hungers for flesh

Environment: Anywhere in the ocean

Health: 12

Damage Inflicted: 5 points

Armor: 5

Movement: Long

Modifications: Speed defense as level 5 due to quickness; stealth as level 5.

Combat: Ebons hunt in loose packs of two or three creatures. When they see or scent something they desire, they zoom toward it, wrap their finned arms and tails around it, and sting it repeatedly with their poisonous vibrissae.

In their first attack, ebons wrap and poison their prey. If this attack is successful, they inflict 1 point of damage, and the poison inflicts 5 points of additional damage (unless the victim succeeds on a Might defense task). Either way, the ebon's grasp increases the difficulty of the victim's next action by one step. In subsequent rounds, ebons bite grabbed prey for 5 points of damage.

Interaction: Ebons are clever predatory animals that do not negotiate. They may flee in the face of a superior show of force, at least until they regroup and return in greater numbers.

Use: As the player characters are engaged in some other activity, they begin to get the sense that something is following them through the water. That sense continues to grow stronger as an ebon hunting pack sidles ever closer.

In some areas of the world, ebons are a myth, a bedtime story to scare children. In those stories, they're called death shades.

GM Intrusion: *Another ebon joins the fight and attacks the character immediately.*

EFFIGY 6 (18)

Effigies are sometimes mistaken for sculptures of humans carved from mottled stone. They can stand motionless for months, years, or even longer before moving. What they're thinking, or even if they're thinking when they aren't moving, isn't clear. But once animate, they can move fluidly and fast, speak intelligently, make alliances, and apparently become invested in human purposes. They never speak of their origins, what manner of creature they are, and what their deeper intentions might be. Because they can phase through solid stone as easily as a human can walk through a doorway, it's difficult to pin down an effigy that doesn't wish to be questioned.

Effigies don't eat normal food. Instead, they consume daily amounts of drit.

Motive: Unknown

Environment: Almost anywhere, but especially underground

Health: 30

Damage Inflicted: 8 points

Armor: 3

Movement: Short; short if phasing through stone

Modifications: Knowledge of the numenera as level 7.

Combat: An effigy often uses cyphers and, if available, an artifact to aid itself in combat. However, it can also hit hard with its stone fists, attacking twice as one action, inflicting 8 points of damage per punch. Alternatively, an effigy can generate a small quake by phasing one hand into the ground. Everyone within short range must succeed on a Might defense task or fall to the ground and take 8 points of damage (from shaking and from being struck by toppling objects, crumbling walls, and so on). Once an effigy triggers a quake, it is dazed for a few rounds and finds the difficulty of all tasks increased by one step.

An effigy flees through the stone rather than fight to the death.

Interaction: Effigies might ignore characters, attack them for reasons they will not reveal, or aid them briefly as if storing up a favor to be called upon later.

Use: A girl in ragged clothing arrives in town with a guardian made of living stone. When the girl is threatened, the guardian defends her, and when the girl sleeps, it stands like a graven statue watching over her. But the girl is wanted for questioning by Aeon Priests in Qi.

Loot: An effigy might carry a couple of cyphers and an artifact.

GM Intrusion: *The effigy tries to grab the character and phase with them through the floor. If successful, it deposits the PC in a sealed hollow underground.*

GM Intrusion: *A character who falls during an effigy-created quake is pinned under a huge piece of granite until they can escape, requiring a difficulty 8 Might-based task by someone else to free them.*

49

ELAAN 5 (15)

Blown by transdimensional winds through parallel planes, elaan are spectral seedlings. From afar they're sometimes visible as drifting motes of pale light that catch on buildings, landscape features, and other creatures like ragged banners. Close up, elaan are revealed as eel-like creatures with disturbingly predatory heads. They cling to living targets, which might not even be aware that they're carrying a phased, nearly invisible passenger. A clinging elaan eventually burrows into its target, where it lays eggs and attempts to influence its host to find a warm, dark, secret corner in which to curl up and wait for the eggs to hatch.

Motive: Reproduction

Environment: Almost anywhere, but more often encountered near population centers

Health: 15

Damage Inflicted: 6 points

Movement: Short when flying

Modifications: Stealth as level 6.

Combat: Elaan are always partially phased, so they're difficult to detect and affect. A character must succeed on a difficulty 6 Intellect task to even notice one nearby. If directly attacked, a character must succeed on a difficulty 6 Might defense task to notice that something partially phased has latched onto them. If the targeted character and their allies fail to notice that something eel-like is trailing the PC like a scarf blowing in the wind, the target gets another attempt at a Might defense task during their next ten-hour recovery, when the elaan attempts to burrow in. If either Might defense task is successful and the target sees the elaan, the target can move, dodge, and jump around enough to frustrate the creature's intention. An elaan eventually gives up and looks for easier prey or, if attacked with weapons that can hurt it (energy or transdimensional attacks), it flees immediately.

An elaan that burrows in is difficult to detect. A character descends one step on the damage track each day the creature is not extracted (possibly by using transdimensional energy, electric shocks, or a similar treatment). In addition, the target must succeed on an Intellect task each hour to remain in their right mind; otherwise, the target attempts to slip away and die in peace. When the character is dead, a clutch of elaan blows out of the body.

Interaction: Elaan are intelligent and may negotiate if communication is opened. They see themselves as refugees from a disaster so ancient they no longer recall what it was. They usually flee creatures who show any ability to harm them.

Use: The PCs see a storm blow into a nearby village or city, one that features strange blips of pale light. If they enter the area, they notice that some of the residents have strange, hard-to-see "scarves" trailing behind them.

GM Intrusion: The character sees that an ally has a strange eel-like creature attached to the back of their neck, like a scarf.

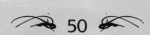

ELDMOR 9 (27)

Eldmorem are dimension-traveling destroyers that arose in a distant parallel dimension. Half living, half automaton, eldmorem lie like cysts between dimensions, only waking from the sleep of ages when disturbed. When that happens, a lone eldmor stretches to its full 200-foot (60 m) length and attempts to trace the traveler's dimensional trajectory back to its plane of origin. If it finds the location, it enacts half-forgotten instructions received millennia earlier and attempts to destroy everything it finds.

Motive: Destroy transdimensional travelers and their planes of origin

Environment: Anywhere dimension walkers begin and end their trips

Health: 50

Damage Inflicted: 12 points

Armor: 5

Movement: Long when flying

Modification: Speed defense as level 6 due to size.

Combat: When "encysted" between dimensions, eldmorem appear like inanimate, weathered boulders the size of small mountains. Upon waking, they unfold to reveal their true shape. Though large, eldmorem can easily discern prey much smaller than themselves.

An eldmor's primary weapons are its eyes, which can emit twin blasts of destructive transdimensional energy at targets within 5 miles (8 km). Each blast inflicts 12 points of damage that phases past normal matter and protective gear (and thus ignores Armor).

Eldmorem can also catch a target that fails a Speed defense task in its manipulators. If a caught target fails an Intellect defense task in the subsequent round, it is ejected from the current reality into a random dimension.

Interaction: Eldmorem can communicate telepathically but mostly choose not to. They are old, weary, and usually motivated to act only because of ancient instructions they half remember.

Use: While traveling across a dimension, the PCs discover that an eldmor completely destroyed a location they visited briefly a few months earlier. This plus a few related clues suggest that something very powerful is slowly hunting the PCs across the dimensions.

Loot: An eldmor corpse can be salvaged for 2d6 cyphers.

The random dimensions where victims of eldmorem sometimes find themselves are not necessarily immediately dangerous, though they can be. The more significant problem for victims is usually finding their way home.

GM Intrusion: *The eldmor summons a dimensional duplicate of the character, which is similar in most ways except it is determined to kill the character.*

Vesied, page 173

Sytor, page 156

ERODEL SHEPHERD   6 (18)

The Erodel is the name of a vanished group of entities that employed slave races, including vesieds and sytors, to extend their own power and influence. The time of the Erodel is gone, but remnants remain. Waking from long stasis, Erodel shepherds still attempt to accrue power and influence even after apocalyptic setbacks from thirty million years earlier. Such persistence in the face of losing everything in the deep past might be considered heroic by some, but most shepherds are probably merely insane.

More than 6 feet (2 m) in diameter, Erodel shepherds look almost like floating trees on which many decorations are hung. Up close, it's clear they are living, mobile creatures, despite the many masks they wear.

Motive: Control

Environment: Almost anywhere, usually accompanied by psychically controlled servitors

Health: 18

Damage Inflicted: 6 points

Armor: 2

Movement: Short; long while flying

Modifications: Resists all mental attacks as level 8.

Combat: Erodel shepherds can batter foes with their limbs, but their true strength is in their ability to mentally control others into defending them. A shepherd can make a psychic attack on a creature within short range. On a failed Intellect defense task, the target acts as the shepherd mentally commands on its next action. If the same target is affected by this dominating attack a second time within a minute, the shepherd's mental control lasts for ten hours.

In addition, a shepherd can broadcast a psychic field that extends to short range, filling affected targets with calm love. An affected target breaks off attacks on the shepherd, lays down their weapons, and cajoles other combatants attacking the shepherd to do the same. Using this field is not an action for the shepherd, but the field affects only one creature in a given round.

Interaction: A shepherd can communicate telepathically with characters within short range. It tries to mentally dominate whomever it runs across and negotiates only with characters that are strong enough to harm it.

Use: An Erodel shepherd should be a dangerous foe, even against high-tier PCs, because most shepherds surround themselves with compliant level 4 servitors.

Loot: Defeated servitors may carry cyphers and even an artifact or two.

GM Intrusion: *More servitors join the conflict.*

EXIGEN 4 (12)

Among the bizarre dimensions is a class of planes called mirror dimensions. Mirror dimensions exist side by side with normal dimensions, but they are not parallel worlds. They are more akin to a parasitic fungus covering a tree. And within that parasitic layer, alien creatures called exigens roam, plucking creatures out of the base plane who usually have no idea they are being stalked.

In practice, exigens are out of phase while they remain in their mirror dimension, and most of the time completely undetectable. But when they stretch their long, reflective limbs into existence to grab prey, they seem to emerge from a shimmering, reflective surface hanging in midair. That's usually the only time they are vulnerable.

Exigens don't eat the creatures they catch, but instead set them loose in the mirror dimension, treating them like pets that can never get free.

Motive: Hungers for companionship

Environment: Anywhere

Health: 15

Damage Inflicted: 5 points

Movement: Short

Modifications: All tasks related to stealth as level 6.

Combat: An exigen stalks potential targets by following them from the safety of their mirror dimension for a period of a few hours or days. Particularly observant targets may notice a few reflective shimmers in the air from time to time, but the significance of those shimmers isn't immediately clear—until an exigen reaches through a shimmer and attempts to grab a target. An attacking exigen becomes visible for a few rounds as it attempts to snatch prey from the base dimension, during which time it is vulnerable.

A target damaged by an exigen must succeed on a Might defense task or be pulled through the interface. Once a target is pulled through, the exigen releases it and offers no further aggression unless attacked by the target. Otherwise, the target is free to act as it wishes, though it remains trapped in the mirror dimension until it can find some way to escape (a difficulty 6 Intellect task) or it dies.

Interaction: An exigen is alien, but if communication can be opened, negotiation might convince it to return a victim to the base dimension or help those in a bad situation to escape into the mirror dimension for safety.

Use: Several notorious criminals held in a sealed cell managed to escape as if into thin air. The only clue is that the guards claim they saw an odd reflective shimmer in the air immediately preceding the breakout.

GM Intrusion: *The character in the mirror dimension who attacks the exigen discovers that the creature has a limited ability to control the dimension. For instance, the exigen can make the entire dimension fold, turning the floor into a cliff face, sending the PC on a fall of more than 50 feet (15 m) on a failed Speed defense task to hold on.*

FARADAWK

Looking like a creature of the sea with wide "wings" and a trailing tail, faradawks skim through the sky, burning shapes of energy rather than living flesh. Faradawks hunt like other animals of prey but are drawn to those carrying items rich in energy, including cyphers and artifacts.

When a faradawk dies, either from violence or old age (faradawks usually live for only a few years), they typically detonate. Within a few days, they might "malfunction" to produce a newly born faradawk.

Motive: Hungers for energy

Environment: Almost anywhere, alone or in groups of three to nine

Health: 6

Damage Inflicted: 3 points

Movement: Immediate; long when flying

Modifications: Speed defense as level 4 due to small size.

Combat: A faradawk prefers to feed on items rich in energy, but if hungry, it attacks living targets who carry such objects. A faradawk's lashing tail inflicts 3 points of damage and sets the victim on fire, inflicting 1 point of damage each round until the victim uses an action to douse the flame. Someone who is so attacked by a faradawk must also succeed on an Intellect defense task or a cypher they carry is drained of its energy and rendered useless.

If three or more faradawks attack a single target, they act like a single level 4 creature that inflicts 5 points of damage.

A faradawk that is killed detonates in a fiery blast of energy, inflicting 6 points of damage on all creatures (except other faradawks) in immediate range.

Interaction: A faradawk behaves almost like a predatory animal, which means it can sometimes be trained by those willing to sacrifice enough energy-rich items to keep the creature satisfied.

Use: Streaks burning through the sky toward the characters are finally revealed as gliding, ray-like creatures of glowing energy.

Certain ruins are prone to producing faradawks from inexplicable machinery that only partially functions.

GM Intrusion: *The character's cypher produces a faradawk instead of its expected effect. However, the faradawk might follow the character around like a pet for a few weeks or longer.*

FLAW   5 (15)

A flaw is easily mistaken for a person at a distance, though perhaps one with a limp or an irregular gait. Close up, it's apparent they've undergone some kind of accident or procedure that left them in a stitched-together state of mismatched skin, extra (or missing) limbs, missing (or extra) eyes or mouths, and a stretched, not-quite human face.

Flaws speak in broken sentences, asking for help, attacking without an obvious reason, or fleeing something that isn't apparent. Where they come from, what their purpose might be, and their ultimate fate isn't apparent, even when someone tries to track down such information.

Motive: Unpredictable

Environment: Almost anywhere, but often in large cities where they can go unnoticed for a time

Health: 20

Damage Inflicted: 6 points

Armor: 1

Movement: Long

Modifications: Deception as level 7.

Combat: A flaw can draw a weapon from apparently nowhere and use it as an action, be that a large maul, a weapon that fires energy, or a detonation. They can also move up to a long distance by taking a single step, and thus position themselves well to attack or evade a fight.

A flaw affects reality in its vicinity, usually to the detriment of its foes. For instance, the ground under a foe's feet may become soft and mushy, restricting movement. The air may become smoky and harsh, making breathing difficult and obscuring sight lines. A character's weapon might become so slippery that they risk dropping it. And so on.

Interaction: Flaws seem incomplete and perhaps insane. They might simply be so alien that humans can't effectively communicate with them. Flaws are not necessarily aggressive, unless first attacked. But they may undertake tasks that don't seem to make sense, and that seem likely to endanger the characters or others.

Use: A flaw is using strange devices to cut a hole in a protective city wall, and all the locals who tried to stop it have gone missing.

Loot: A flaw may carry several cyphers.

Flaws can seemingly "create" objects by desire alone, but they might actually be drawing them from a phased space or an alternate dimension. In practice, there's little difference.

GM Intrusion: *Something completely unexpected occurs, such as the air around the character solidifying into amber, trapping the PC until they can escape.*

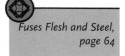

FUSER 6 (18)

Some humans experiment with fusing flesh and steel and have some of their organic parts replaced with artificial components. Usually, everything works as expected, and whether the components are beneath the skin or actually replace the skin, that human gains many benefits from the change. But sometimes, a living body rejects replacement parts, or parts malfunction. This has maladaptive effects on a subject's mind, eventually rendering them insane. Dangerous and unpredictable, fusers seek to continually modify themselves with parts until they resemble some sort of machine nightmare, with only a few original human parts visible amid the metal and synth.

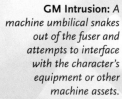

Fuses Flesh and Steel, page 64

Motive: Unpredictable

Environment: Almost anywhere

Health: 27

Damage Inflicted: 8 points

Armor: 2

Movement: Short; long when jumping

Modifications: Tasks related to interfacing with or talking to machines as level 8.

Combat: A fuser might seem rational one moment, then with an audible click become a murderous sociopath the next, which means they might attack with surprise. A fuser usually has some kind of weapon built into its modified body, which might be a machine sword or a ray-emitting artifact. Because of its quickness, a fuser can attack two foes as one action.

A fuser can also jump up to a long distance as part of its movement, which might allow it to close in to attack or escape if things are going poorly. Many fusers enjoy a low-level self-repair capability, which restores 1 point of health per round.

Interaction: Fusers are insane, made so by their augmentations. Removing the augmentations is probably the only way to calm a fuser's mind, but no fuser would agree to that.

GM Intrusion: A machine umbilical snakes out of the fuser and attempts to interface with the character's equipment or other machine assets.

Use: An NPC who Fuses Flesh and Steel becomes damaged in a fight or because of a malfunction from a cypher the characters provided, and goes from placid to fuser.

Loot: A fuser's form usually contains two or three cyphers.

GAPHELIN
7 (21)

Weird rock formations are common in the Ninth World. Sometimes those rocks are even weirder than they first appear. Gaphelin are "rock" pillars that emerge overnight, standing 9 to 15 feet (3 to 5 m) tall, and shot through with purple crystal. Standing alone or in small groups, gaphelin are usually discovered near locations that contain ruins of the prior worlds, where nanos have used their abilities to effect change, or where many cyphers are stored or have been recently used. No one has ever seen gaphelin appear or disappear. One day they're simply there, as if they had always been. A few minutes, hours, or days later, and they're gone, disappearing in the space of an eyeblink.

Motive: Exploration

Environment: Anywhere they can emerge from the ground, alone or in formations of three to five

Health: 21

Damage Inflicted: 9 points

Armor: 5

Movement: Immobile (but can appear or disappear up to once per hour when unobserved)

Modifications: Knowledge of the numenera as level 8.

Combat: If a gaphelin spends an action charging its crystalline interior with psychic energy, in the following round it can make a psychic attack on a creature within long range that inflicts 9 points of Intellect damage (ignores Armor). If the gaphelin doesn't spend the round charging up, the 9 points of damage are deflected normally by Armor.

A gaphelin can telekinetically manipulate objects within short range.

A gaphelin can also cause portions of the ground around it within long range to detonate near foes. Effects of that detonation vary as follows against creatures that unsuccessfully defend themselves.

1	Creates a level 7 force bubble protecting/trapping targets in an immediate radius for one minute.
2	Sends creatures in an immediate radius into an alternate dimension.
3	Puts creatures within immediate range to sleep for one minute.
4	Inflicts 7 points of shrapnel damage in a short radius.
5	Fixes everything in place in an immediate radius.
6	One creature within immediate range is turned to stone.

Interaction: Gaphelin generally aren't aggressive unless first attacked. The creatures speak telepathically but lack syntax and common references. They question basic assumptions but assume advanced knowledge in other areas.

Use: Upon waking up after taking a ten-hour recovery, the PCs discover a strange new rock formation at the edge of their camp. Some of their cyphers are missing, and the items are found broken and used up around the base of the pillar.

Loot: A "dead" gaphelin contains 1d6 crystalline cyphers.

GM Intrusion: *The character receives a mental image (from the gaphelin) of a strange, otherworldly location containing a huge crystalline machine. The image is so overwhelming and inexplicable that the PC loses their next turn.*

GEVANIC
6 (18)

A pulsing, bluish synth sphere about 15 feet (5 m) in diameter, a gevanic's surface constantly ripples and deforms. It is an automaton found in drifting ruins lost in the night or structures dotted here and there across the continent. Inveterate samplers, gevanics constantly seek small devices, machine parts, portions of other automatons, and even nips of living creatures, which they seal away within one of the many swirling metallic spheres making up the entity.

Sometimes strange singing can be heard faintly near a gevanic, music that seems coordinated with the pulsing of its surface. Those who hear the singing later suffer from odd and unsettling dreams.

Motive: Seeks fresh samples

Environment: Anywhere

Health: 36

Damage Inflicted: 6 points

Armor: 3

Movement: Short when flying

Modifications: Speed defense as level 5 due to size and speed.

Combat: When first encountered, this automaton swirls forward, which might be construed as an attack, but which is actually a sample-gathering exercise. A nip of flesh tucked into a sphere inflicts 1 or 2 points of damage at most, then the gevanic moves on.

However, if resisted, the gevanic becomes aggressive. It can attack all creatures within immediate range by "flailing" its metallic spheres in a flurry, inflicting 6 points of damage to each victim. In addition, the touch of a sampling sphere from an aggressive gevanic disrupts nervous systems. Anyone who is struck by one must make a Might defense task; those who fail are stunned and lose their next turn.

Interaction: Creatures who allow a gevanic to sample their flesh and their items have nothing to worry about, but those who resist are attacked. Otherwise, a gevanic doesn't seem to have any use for negotiation. If targets stop resisting, a gevanic may stop trying to subdue them.

Use: Gevanics are weird and dangerous foes encountered in space or in ancient ruins. They never grow tired of sampling, so when one moves into an area, it quickly moves through it, ejecting previously sampled bits in favor of fresh material.

Loot: A destroyed gevanic leaves behind a clutch of small metallic spheres in which valuables can be found, including 1d20 oddities, 1d6 cyphers, and a few oddities, though this also entails looking through pieces of rotting flesh and dissected organs from other sample containers.

GM Intrusion: *The gevanic sampling sphere snatches the character's cypher and swirls away if the PC does not succeed on a Speed defense task.*

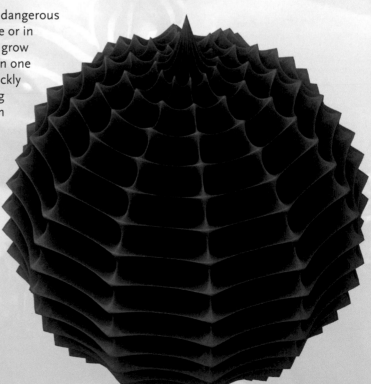

GHRU   3 (9)

Ghru look very much like pale humans with large heads that resemble strange numenera devices, with glass panels for faces. On these panels, they project the image of a human face that speaks and makes expressions as a human would. Thus, ghru are humans with machine minds.

Ghru possess biomechanical brains they built in a processing plant that is more like a temple. Thus, they have certain skills and knowledge from their inception, but only some of it is useful. Despite this, ghru have an understanding of machines and advanced knowledge like medicine, biology, and various machine sciences.

Motive: Defense

Environment: Anywhere machines still function

Health: 12

Damage Inflicted: 7 points

Armor: 1

Movement: Short

Modifications: Knowledge of machines as level 6; seeing through lies or tricks as level 2.

Combat: Ghru warriors wield storm staves, medium melee artifact weapons that inflict 3 additional points of damage from electricity. (A storm staff can also hurl short-range bolts of red lightning that inflict 5 points of damage.) Ghru also employ poison against their enemies whenever possible. For the ghru, sometimes a warrior is one who employs stealth to get close to an enemy and strike with a poisoned fingertip needle rather than a burly armored figure with a massive weapon.

Ghru armor is derived from an artifact called electric armor that also inflicts 1 point of damage on any creature that strikes the ghru in combat.

Interaction: It is difficult for a ghru brain to learn much beyond what it is initially given. The ghru have fine memories and store new information, but they do not adapt well.

Use: A biomechanical brain processing plant vital for the ghru's continued existence has malfunctioned. Ghru are traveling everywhere looking for items to repair it, but they have an incomplete knowledge of what they need.

Loot: A ghru might carry one or more artifacts, including a storm staff and electric armor, described above (depletion: 1 in 1d10).

Ghru are found mostly on a planet called Naharrai, farther from the sun than Earth, but sometimes they show up in the Ninth World through the use of strange devices or craft.

GM Intrusion: *The ghru uses a level 3 artifact in the form of an animate mechanical glove that holds the character in place until they can escape.*

GLAUXIM   5 (15)

Handprints that reappear on walls no matter how many times the previous set is washed away, children or the elderly with new fragments of memory that are not their own, extreme drowsiness dropping the locals into unplanned naps, and so on are mysterious and frightening. A glauxim might be the cause. Inexplicable events, weird marks, and unsettling dreams could mean that a glauxim is nearby, affecting reality in a variety of ways.

A glauxim is a snakelike creature about 9 feet (3 m) in length that is both alive and partly made of sleek devices of the numenera. Once seen and identified, a glauxim leaves an area in search of fresh victims.

Motive: Unknown

Environment: Anywhere

Health: 18

Damage Inflicted: 6 points

Armor: 3

Movement: Short

Modifications: All tasks related to perception and stealth as level 7.

Combat: A glauxim usually avoids direct combat by staying hidden and relying on its long-range improbability field. The field has two levels of effect. Normally, the field causes random odd happenings in the area, troubling targets for several days or months with unsettling dreams, extreme runs of bad luck, mysterious marks, strange sounds, and so on.

But if a glauxim's secret presence is threatened, it can directly manipulate reality to cause walls to collapse on foes, weapons to go off unexpectedly, cyphers to detonate, brains to drop into sleep, and so on, generally creating one level 5 effect within long range per round. Whenever a glauxim creates such a directed effect, its entire body glows with a soft blue illumination.

Interaction: Direct communication with a glauxim doesn't seem possible, but indirect communication from a series of dreams had by an NPC, memories recovered by an ally, or strange marks could lead the PCs to something dangerous, but potentially of great interest.

Use: A village believes it is suffering under the curse of an evil sorcerer who lives in the ruin at the edge of town. In truth, the "sorcerer" (an Aeon Priest) is also being negatively affected by the glauxim's odd aura.

Loot: A glauxim's body could be salvaged for a couple of cyphers.

GM Intrusion: *The character suddenly recalls a traumatic event despite the fact that the event never happened to them, but to someone who lived in a foreign place who might not even have been human. The character must succeed on an Intellect defense task or be stunned and lose their next turn. Regardless, the memory remains.*

GLERESISK   4 (12)

The blubbery, foam-like flesh of a floating gleresisk might be mistaken for seed pods of a particularly large plant blowing in the wind—until one turns against the wind and dives for the head of freshly perceived prey. The head-sized mass of yellowish floating goo, with its parade of trailing tendrils, absorbs minds by physically sucking brain matter into itself. The victim's knowledge and memories become the gleresisk's. When it eats a mind, it becomes a conscious and intelligent creature for one day, during which time it can plan, pick up previously conceived projects, and so on, until it metabolizes the stolen brain tissue and once again reverts to a predator with merely animal instincts.

Motive: Hungers for fresh minds

Environment: Anywhere alone, or in flocks of three to ten

Health: 12

Damage Inflicted: 4 points

Movement: Immediate; long when flying

Modifications: Speed defense as level 5 due to size.

Combat: A gleresisk dives at prey and attacks with its nest of tendrils. A victim must succeed on a Speed defense task or take 4 points of damage. If it inflicts damage, the gleresisk retains its hold on the victim until the victim can escape. Each round, a victim held fast in a gleresisk's tendrils takes 4 points of Intellect damage (ignores Armor). A victim who dies from this damage is mentally consumed by the gleresisk. The body collapses, and the gleresisk floats away, satisfied.

Interaction: A gleresisk can mimic speech and even act with the motivations of someone's mind who was recently consumed, but that's just a ruse. It has its own agenda, which probably involves methods of securing future minds on which to feed in relative safety.

Use: The mind of an Aeon Priest with vital information was consumed by a swarm of three gleresisks. Capturing those creatures and quizzing the fractured, failing mind of the dead person is a mission only a few could manage.

A swarm of four or more gleresisks can attack as a single level 6 creature inflicting 6 points of damage.

GM Intrusion: The character has a terrible dream that they are the animating intelligence in a gleresisk, but their intelligence will persist for only so long. But what if it isn't a dream?

GOLDEN CACHINNATE   5 (15)

Vividly yellow, a golden cachinnate is about the size of a human, but it's obviously something far more dangerous. Its wide mouth always yawns in a predator's grin, and it's usually laughing with obvious glee. Its bulbous eyes see everything. And the golden hue of its skin is so odiferous that it seems to steam with acidic malice.

In this case, looks do not deceive. A golden cachinnate is always secreting toxin into the air from its skin and internally. Its touch is death, but so is its breath. Even those who spend too much time near one are in peril. The constant laughing is maddening, but it only distracts a victim from noticing that they are dying.

Motive: Hungers for flesh

Environment: Usually in wooded areas

Health: 25

Damage Inflicted: 5 points

Armor: 1

Movement: Short; short when leaping

Combat: Targets touched by a golden cachinnate must succeed on a Might defense task or take 5 points of Speed damage (ignores Armor) from toxin. Each round thereafter, the toxin continues to inflict 2 points of Speed damage until the victim succeeds at a Might defense task.

In addition, every creature within immediate range of a golden cachinnate must succeed on a Might defense task each round or take 1 point of Speed damage (ignores Armor) from the toxin in the air exhaled by the creature.

Finally, a golden cachinnate can spit toxic darts at targets within long range who are affected as if they were touched by the creature.

Interaction: These creatures are predators. They're clever, but not intelligent.

Use: A group of abhumans hunts golden cachinnates to harvest the creatures' poison for their own use. This sometimes causes wounded golden cachinnates to flee into areas settled by expanding human settlements.

GM Intrusion: *The character who takes poison damage must succeed on an Intellect defense task or become incapacitated by overwhelming hilarity. Unless the PC can succeed on an Intellect task to escape the effect, they eventually die laughing.*

HANEEK 4 (12)

A haneek is a hungry predator, but it sometimes "adopts" a character and merely follows them around, rather than trying to eat them. It hunts other creatures around the followed character instead. Because haneek are hard to spot, it's often not initially apparent what's going on.

Haneek are essentially sheets of almost transparent tissue that pass light with hardly any distortion. They can twist and fold themselves to move about like sidewinding snakes, gallop on faux limbs, and can even flap and glide through the air. Regardless of their shape, they smell a bit like rotting food, which is often the only warning those being hunted by a haneek have before the layer of hungry tissue drops on them (or victims walk into a haneek that's positioned itself in a doorway).

Once a victim is ensnared by a haneek, flesh-to-tissue contact begins to digest the prey. This sends a bloom of scarlet radiating through the haneek's body, rendering it briefly visible as it feeds.

Motive: Hungers for flesh

Environment: Anywhere near places humans live

Health: 16

Damage Inflicted: 4 points

Movement: Short; short when gliding

Modifications: Stealth tasks as level 7; stealth tasks as level 3 for up to an hour after it has fed.

Combat: A haneek prefers that victims ensnare themselves by failing to notice it poised before them. Otherwise it can lash out with a flap of tissue. Either way, a victim must succeed on a Might defense task or become stuck to the haneek until it can escape. Each round a victim remains stuck to a haneek, it suffers 4 points of damage (ignores Armor) as the direct contact begins to digest the victim.

Even after a victim escapes, a runaway digestive process continues to inflict 1 point of damage (ignores Armor) each round, until the victim can come up with some sort of treatment or, more likely, cut off the afflicted patch of skin. Best case, this self-mutilation inflicts 4 points of damage (ignores Armor) that leaves a nasty scar. Worst case, the victim must sacrifice a limb.

Interaction: Haneek seem somewhat intelligent, but they do not communicate or seem to have a language.

Use: The PCs encounter an NPC who doesn't realize a haneek "guardian" is following them about.

GM Intrusion: *The haneek just attacked by the character splits into two level 3 haneek.*

Heeldra mucus huts pock the hulls of some large ships like barnacles, and prey on the crew and passengers.

HEELDRAN 2 (6)

Able to breathe in both air and water, heeldra are an aquatic abhuman race that builds dens out of hardened self-secreted mucus. Heeldra communities are usually in out-of-the-way places that are still close enough to human dwellings that heeldra infiltrators can steal away children, the old, and those otherwise too weak to defend themselves. The heeldra will eat most anything, but they prefer human meat.

Heeldra don't speak; they communicate with each other via mucus discharge. This not only disgusts other creatures but also can physically impair those close enough to smell it (or come in contact with diffusing mucus, if underwater).

Motive: Hungers for flesh

Environment: Small communities dwell near the shore

Health: 9

Damage Inflicted: 3 points

Movement: Short; long when swimming

Modifications: Perception and deception as level 5.

Combat: Heeldra prefer to fight with spears. They like to attack with surprise, rising from the water (even apparently shallow pools or runoff) in an attempt to catch their target unawares. In the face of stiff resistance, they flee back to the water (or, if in the water, onto dry land).

Heeldra mucus discharge is constant, providing an asset to any swimming task, a barrier against dryness while they are above water, and a means of communication.

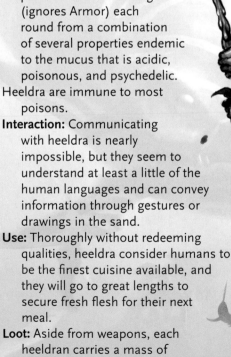

However, creatures within immediate range that contact the mucus via smell or diffusion take 1 point of Intellect damage (ignores Armor) each round from a combination of several properties endemic to the mucus that is acidic, poisonous, and psychedelic.

Heeldra are immune to most poisons.

Interaction: Communicating with heeldra is nearly impossible, but they seem to understand at least a little of the human languages and can convey information through gestures or drawings in the sand.

Use: Thoroughly without redeeming qualities, heeldra consider humans to be the finest cuisine available, and they will go to great lengths to secure fresh flesh for their next meal.

Loot: Aside from weapons, each heeldran carries a mass of collected valuables in a hardened mucus pocket. Items include strangely shaped fish bones, broken pieces of ancient devices, and usually 1d6 shins.

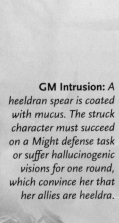

GM Intrusion: A heeldran spear is coated with mucus. The struck character must succeed on a Might defense task or suffer hallucinogenic visions for one round, which convince her that her allies are heeldra.

HUNGRY PENNON   4 (12)

If a group of bandits, mercenaries, or vicious abhumans advances under a flapping standard of war that doesn't actually seem to be connected to a pole, but rather hangs free-floating above one of the combatants, it's probably not a flag but a hungry pennon. Hungry pennons are symbiotic beings that psychically attach themselves to another creature, the more aggressive and intelligent the better.

The creature to which a hungry pennon makes this attachment may at first value the advantages provided. But over time, the pennon gains mental ascendancy. The hungry pennon wants to feed, and it prefers to scavenge the bodies of freshly killed prey. Thus, it drives its host (or hosts) into more frequent and more vicious conflicts.

If the host is killed, the hungry pennon may flap away, or it may proposition a new host, who must freely accept it before a connection is made.

Motive: Hungers for flesh

Environment: Anywhere

Health: 18

Damage Inflicted: 4 points

Movement: Short when flying

Modifications: Perception as level 6.

Combat: A hungry pennon attempts to flee from direct combat by flying away. If it has no other option, it bites a foe with the tiny mouths it hides under the folds of its banner-like wings.

A hungry pennon takes down prey by convincing its host to attack a target. Fresh hosts must succeed on an Intellect defense task to avoid the suggestion to attack an arbitrary creature selected by the hungry pennon as its next meal. The difficulty of all attacks made by a host with a bonded pennon is reduced by one step, which explains the attraction to the initial psychic connection.

A pennon never willingly leaves a bonded host. A host who has had enough of the bond must succeed on a difficulty 6 Intellect task each time it wants to attack the pennon. However, a host who remains bonded to a hungry pennon for more than a month eventually has no choice but to act as the pennon's puppet in all things. If a hungry pennon is killed, its bonded host suffers 6 points of Intellect damage (ignores Armor).

Interaction: A hungry pennon may communicate via telepathic images to creatures within immediate range, getting across its desire to bond by sharing images of it and its host being gloriously victorious in combat.

Use: The PCs fight abhumans, one of whom seems to fly a war banner. If victorious, the PCs can take the sentient war standard for themselves.

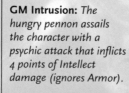

GM Intrusion: The hungry pennon assails the character with a psychic attack that inflicts 4 points of Intellect damage (ignores Armor).

IANI 4 (12)

The iani are evolved mechanisms with both mechanical and biological aspects. They have the ability to absorb mechanical devices and assimilate them into their bodies. After dwelling motionless in dark caverns for millennia, the iani have begun venturing out onto the surface. They are looking for specific devices that they call "the Legacy," though no one but the iani understands what that means. Sometimes the iani steal objects of the numenera they encounter, hoping that those objects turn out to be part of the Legacy.

Quadrupeds, the iani appear as a combination of living creatures and sleek automatons slighter larger than a human.

Motive: Find "the Legacy" by investigating any and all unknown artifacts

Environment: Anywhere, often in groups of four or more

Health: 12

Damage Inflicted: 4 points

Armor: 2

Movement: Long

Modifications: Speed defense, jumping, and balancing as level 5.

Combat: While iani have claws they can use to batter and cut foes, they rely on technological devices they've absorbed. As an action, an iani can absorb any device it touches. As another action, it can use the absorbed device (if applicable) as though the device were a natural part of it. Given ten minutes, it can transfer the abilities of the absorbed device to all iani within 3 miles (5 km). It can also reject a previously absorbed device and spew it out again, good as new.

Cyphers can be used only once, and abilities don't always transfer, but absorbed artifacts can be used multiple times and their abilities can be shared among other iani.

Interaction: Iani do not grow personally attached to absorbed devices that turn out not to be part of the Legacy, and they return such objects if the PCs open lines of communication and offer something in return. But their outlook is almost incomprehensible to humans, and communication is difficult, as they speak no human languages. Their tongue is more of a machine language, composed of tones of various pitches and lengths. They are extraordinarily intelligent, however, and can interpret much from gestures and whatnot, and they can quickly pick up the basics of a written language, which they can scrawl in the dirt.

Use: The iani, hoping to find an object of the Legacy, steal a device that a small village depends on for food, water, or some other vital service, and retreat to a lair in nearby ruins.

Loot: Iani typically contain a couple of cyphers and possibly an artifact.

If characters somehow achieve a good relationship with them, the iani might ask for help. The PCs can provide useful guidance as the creatures venture out into a world that is utterly alien to them.

GM Intrusion: *The iani has absorbed a magnetic pulse device. The character's metal weapon is ripped from their hand and tossed a short distance away. If the character is wearing metal armor, they are tossed backward an immediate distance, knocked prone, and suffer 1 point of ambient damage.*

ICE WEAVER 3 (9)

Delicate, lattice-like ice structures created by ice weavers are often mistaken as some kind of manifestation of the prior worlds. But these structures usually last only a few days or months before cracking, breaking, and melting away.

When a pack of ice weaver hunters moves into a new area, they first construct a redoubt of woven ice. When explorers or residents of isolated communities find such "ice castles," they should beware. Ice weavers are near. Luckily the creatures never stay in the same area long.

Ice weavers absorb heat and excrete ice. About 12 feet (4 m) long, these low-slung predators are clad in frost scales, complete with many transparent spikes and barbs. Condensation vapor often swirls from their super-cold bodies, and they race along the ground by producing a layer of ice along which they can slide.

Motive: Hungers for flesh

Environment: Almost anywhere in packs of three to eight

Health: 9

Damage Inflicted: 4 points

Armor: 4 (see Combat)

Movement: Long

Modifications: Speed defense as level 4.

Combat: Ice weavers race quickly on self-created narrow lanes of ice and use that speed to their advantage in combat. An ice weaver can move a long distance and attack as a single action. It can also use its action to create a lane that stretches up above the heads of its prey, so that they can't reach it that round unless they try to climb an elevated, slippery ice lane (a difficulty 6 Might task).

When an ice weaver bites down on a foe, it drains heat and inflicts 4 points of Speed damage (ignores Armor). Completely frozen victims are dragged off and consumed later.

Anyone within immediate range of an ice weaver suffers 1 point of cold damage each round.

Interaction: Ice weavers are intelligent, but they prize hunting more than almost any other activity. Excess frozen prey is stored in lairs hidden in high glaciers, where ice weaver young are reared. Someone threatening a supply of frozen food or a weaver lair could get a pack to back off or move away from an area.

Use: Characters hear about a "prior-world ruin" that appeared without warning. When they investigate, they find no ruin, but the small village nearby is vacated and empty. The only clue about what happened is a muddy trail leading north.

Ice lanes are level 3 and melt in under an hour in warm conditions.

GM Intrusion: *The character must succeed on a difficulty 4 Speed defense task, or slip and fall hard (taking 1 point of damage) on an ice trail left by an ice weaver.*

IDYC 5 (15)

Disgusting, unexplainable, and appallingly affectionate, the 9-foot (3 m) long sliding biomechanical entity known as an idyc roams the fringes of civilization. Its unfortunate behavior depends on the health of those it encounters. Creatures who are hurt or wounded are not bothered by the idyc unless they first provoke it. Healthy creatures find the attention of the idyc actively dangerous.

Motive: Reproduction

Environment: Anywhere (always outside)

Health: 19

Damage Inflicted: 3 points

Armor: 2

Movement: Short; short when climbing or swimming

Combat: The idyc's abilities and outlook are based on the initial health of those it encounters. It targets initially healthy creatures in hopes of finding robust hosts for its young.

Healthy: Attacks immediately with a shower of short-range darts (up to four as a single action) and then attempts to break off the engagement. Victims struck by a dart must succeed on an additional Might defense task. On a failure, the embedded dart digs deeper into the tissue and becomes impossible to find and extract without a special operation. Sometime over the following three days, the victim writhes and releases 1d6 tiny level 1 idycs. This inflicts 3 points of damage per idyc so hatched. If the victim survives, they feel protective of the newly hatched creatures. The child idycs attempt to go on their way.

Hurt: Attempts friendly interaction. This could occur even after the idyc has hurt a previously healthy victim with darts.

Interaction: The idyc is happy to speak to those who are hurt or diseased, and therefore of no reproductive interest to it. It speaks a variety of languages in an obviously artificial voice, and seems particularly fond of songs, prose, and poems about love and friendship. It doesn't reveal that its darts are eggs.

Use: Ideally, the PCs encounter an idyc the first time when they are hurt, and later when they are healthy (or vice versa). Maybe they believe they have befriended it, but it attacks when they show themselves capable of tending to their injuries.

Loot: Scavengers can find 1d10 shins, a few cyphers, and one or two oddities in the wreckage of a destroyed idyc.

GM Intrusion: *A destroyed idyc releases one last barrage of rocky darts at all creatures within short range.*

IGOTHUS 3 (9)

The desert is a harsh place, and creatures adapted for its harshness are usually . . . harsh. Igothus are no exception. They are abhumans able to go long periods without food or water. When they do find prey, however, they fall upon it with reckless and savage abandon. They don't just kill to eat—they enjoy it. They are cruel sadists and awful murderers, and pain and hunger are all they understand. As a group, they have no hierarchy and keep no semblance of order. They are more akin to a swarm of insects than a band of humans or even a pack of hounds.

Igothus eat anything organic. They generally do not kill each other, but they eat their dead if given the opportunity.

Motive: Hungers for flesh; murder and cruelty

Environment: Hot, dry areas

Health: 9

Damage Inflicted: 4 points

Armor: 1

Movement: Short

Modifications: Speed defense as level 4.

Combat: Igothus are fast and agile, savagely attacking with claws and teeth. They never use weapons or armor, and they prefer swarm tactics. A group of five igothus can attack as a single individual of level 5, inflicting 8 points of damage.

Igothus seem to be utterly fearless and fight with a savage bloodlust to their dying breath. In the moment in which it is struck down, an igothus can often make a single, final attack if it has the opportunity.

Interaction: Igothus do not have their own language, typically speaking just enough of the predominant language of the surrounding area to communicate basic concepts to each other: "Look, meat!" "Many foes."

Use: In Vralk, people capture and enslave igothus, turning them into weapons of war. Typically, Vralkans keep the abhumans in pits or inside cages on wagons, loosing them upon the enemy when the moment is right.

Vralk, a harsh region poisoned by volcanic heat and ash, lies north of the Clock of Kala. Its human inhabitants are similarly brutal and violent.

Clock of Kala, page 213

GM Intrusion: *The character's attack on the igothus was successful, but the savage creature immediately throws a handful of its own blood in the PC's face, momentarily blinding the target for one round while it makes its own attack.*

IMORPHIN GONOPH   5 (15)

A mass of glowing, nested spheres that trail coiling tendrils, an imorphin gonoph is a living creature about the size of a human. These floating creatures are sometimes mistaken for bits of architecture broken off from ruins of the prior worlds, since they might not stir for days at a time. In fact, they've been known to serve as lamps in human villages where the residents don't know the creatures' true natures.

That nature is revealed when the spheres occasionally expand to reveal a variety of cavities, some of which are empty and some of which contain blinking eyes. The creature uses its tendrils in an attempt to pilfer valuables from lone travelers or small groups moving about at night. Valuables, from the perspective of an imorphin gonoph, include clothing, hats, packs, or really any artificial item (up to and including weapons, cyphers, and artifacts). The creature stuffs each stolen item into a gaping cavity, then closes it. Most stolen objects are never seen again.

Motive: Steals

Environment: Anywhere humans gather in large numbers

Health: 23

Damage Inflicted: 5 points

Armor: 2

Movement: Flies an immediate distance each round

Modifications: Stealth as level 7.

Combat: Imorphin gonophs don't move quickly, so anyone who wants to break off combat with one can usually do so by moving out of range. An imorphin gonoph rarely pursues. Normally it attacks only if attacked first (usually by a victim who doesn't appreciate having their equipment stolen).

GM Intrusion: *Striking the imorphin gonoph causes the creature to immediately emit a sonic attack as an extra action.*

In addition to lashing a target with its tendrils to inflict 5 points of damage, a gonoph can reveal a cavity resembling a large mouth that emits piercing sonic effects, including the following:

Sonic barrage that inflicts 5 points of damage on all targets within immediate range

Piercing sonic ray that inflicts 5 points of damage (ignores Armor) on one target within short range

Reverberation that deafens all characters within short range who fail a Might defense roll. Each round, they can attempt another Might defense roll to shrug off the effect.

Interaction: Meaningful interaction with an imorphin gonoph continues to elude anyone who tries it. But sometimes one of these creatures will accept a gift and break off a conflict.

Use: The handful of strange floating lamps in the small village sets it apart from others, but the locals refuse to answer questions regarding their weird light sources.

Loot: A defeated imorphin gonoph sometimes disgorges recently pilfered items, which can include random pieces of clothing, weapons, and possibly a cypher.

IMUSTEN CRAWLER   5 (15)

The imusten crawler winds its long, flexible body down from an overhanging structure or up from a tunnel or vent in the earth, seeking prey. The creature's diamond-shaped head, crusted with fangs and eyes, isn't nearly as horrific as its ability to cause its victims to secrete a numbing gel that not only holds them in place but also drowns them from the inside as their lungs fill with gel.

An imusten crawler has an inexplicable fear of seskii. When a crawler is in the presence of a seskii (or seskii tracer), the seskii's crystals light up, and the crawler breaks off its attack and wriggles away.

Motive: Hungers for flesh

Environment: Anywhere

Health: 18

Damage Inflicted: 6 points

Armor: 2

Movement: Short; short when climbing; immediate when burrowing

Modifications: Speed defense as level 6 due to quickness.

Combat: An imusten crawler bites prey if the victim fails a Speed defense task, inflicting 6 points of damage. The bitten target must then succeed on a Might defense task, or it feels a numbing, mounting pressure in its lungs, which begin to fill up with smothering gel. The victim takes 6 points of damage (ignores Armor) each round until it succeeds on a Might defense task. Each failed task to cough up the seed gel makes the succeeding defense task one step more difficult as the victim suffocates.

An imusten crawler instead may choose to cause a victim to secrete gel from its skin, holding the victim in place—rather than suffocating it—in a pocket of clear, viscous material. The gel has a soporific effect and can effectively store living creatures indefinitely until the imusten becomes hungry enough to eat.

Interaction: Imusten crawlers are intelligent but secretive. They resist attempts by other creatures to learn more about them and their ultimate origin. They can't speak, but they possess a low-level telepathic ability to communicate basic concepts.

Use: A pocket of gel containing more than a dozen stored humans and abhumans in an underground hollow might indicate that an imusten crawler has been using the space as a larder.

Loot: The discarded equipment of eaten prey sometimes contains valuables, including a few cyphers.

Seskii, page 258

Seskii tracer, page 142

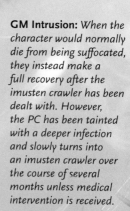

GM Intrusion: *When the character would normally die from being suffocated, they instead make a full recovery after the imusten crawler has been dealt with. However, the PC has been tainted with a deeper infection and slowly turns into an imusten crawler over the course of several months unless medical intervention is received.*

The inconae are active on a vast artificial "world" known as the Gloaming.

INCONA　　　　　　　　　　　　7 (21)

Creatures of darkness and terror, the inconae wormed their way into this universe from somewhere else: an otherworldly realm, it is said, that they devoured entirely.

Many conspiracy theories include the inconae. Some think they are responsible for the vast extent of life in the universe. From the inconae point of view, that's all existence is—a slaughterhouse of waiting cattle.

Inconae can alter their metabolisms and digestive systems to eat literally anything, but their default sustenance is blood. Only when they cannot get blood will they turn to other sources of nourishment, both organic and inorganic. Some people speculate that if need be, they will feed on spacetime itself, eventually consuming the universe.

Motive: Hungers for blood (or other things)

Environment: Anywhere shadowy

Health: 30

Damage Inflicted: 8 points

Armor: 1

Movement: Short

Modifications: Stealth and jumping as level 10.

Combat: Inconae hunt in packs, seeping out from the shadows to devour prey and then receding into the darkness. They attack with tooth and claw, making two melee attacks as a single action.

An incona can also use its action to mesmerize a foe. If the victim fails an Intellect defense task, they suffer 2 points of Intellect damage. Until those points are restored, the victim is confused and disoriented, and the difficulty of their actions is increased by two steps. During this time of confusion, an incona can make a subtle suggestion and the victim will follow it, believing it to be their own idea. The suggested action cannot be something they wouldn't normally do, so committing suicide or murdering a friend are likely right out. The inconae always use far greater subtlety. Their plots and plans are convoluted.

Inconae can see in complete darkness, and they hate bright light. The difficulty of an incona's actions in bright light is increased by one step.

Interaction: Inconae consider all other creatures to be nothing more than prey or feedstock. And they do not entreat with feedstock.

Use: The inconae make excellent villains, and because they work in groups, they can be a direct challenge even for the most powerful PCs.

GM Intrusion: *After striking the character, the incona also destroys or devours a small piece of their equipment that is easily grabbed.*

IXOBRYCHID 7 (21)

Ixobrychids are sometimes found frozen in strange glaciers of the Frozen South or in structures circling high overhead, immobile and insensate for years uncounted. When still immobile, they resemble 6-foot (2 m) tall wrinkled seedpods that are green and black. But if they are carved free of entrapping ice or the ice is melted away, they unfold to reveal awful fractal limbs, wings, tendrils, and teeth, a sight so horrific it can break the minds of those unprepared for such impossibilities.

For the most part, their long hibernation has driven ixobrychids who regain mobility into what seems like insanity. They lash out at other creatures in rage. When left undisturbed, they attempt to build ever more complex devices with no clear purpose.

Motive: Unknown

Environment: Anywhere cold, including the void of space

Health: 28

Damage Inflicted: 7 points

Movement: Immediate; long when flying

Modifications: All tasks related to the numenera as level 9.

Combat: An ixobrychid can make four attacks as a single action using its fractal-like limbs. A damaged target must also succeed on an Intellect defense task or be stunned and lose its next turn.

If an ixobrychid chooses to focus all of its attacks on a single target, and at least two of those attacks hit, the victim must succeed on a Might defense task to pull free. Otherwise the creature folds up around the target, completely covering it. The enfolded target can do nothing but attempt to escape. If the target doesn't escape within a few rounds, the ixobrychid unfolds once more, revealing that the target has vanished. In truth, it's been shunted to a pocket dimension where the ixobrychid collects things of all sorts, many of which defy description.

Interaction: An ixobrychid is too insane (or alien) to communicate with humans, but if telepathic contact succeeds, mind-wrenching vistas are revealed, vistas that make no sense but that the ixobrychid seems happy to share as long as contact is maintained. Such contact is normally damaging to humans and similar minds.

Use: An important person has been "eaten" by an ixobrychid, and the PCs must slay the creature and use its carcass as a key to the pocket dimension where the victim (and many other strange things) is stored.

Loot: An ixobrychid accumulates several cyphers and oddities, and a few artifacts, in its pocket dimension. Accessing that transdimensional space requires an ixobrychid corpse and a successful difficulty 6 Intellect task.

Quover are generally carefree observers, but they flock to fight with suicidal intensity any ixobrychid they discover.

Quover, page 133

GM Intrusion: *The character who sees the ixobrychid unfold must succeed on an Intellect defense task or be stunned by the overwhelming display and lose their next action.*

JACENTWING 1 (3)

A jacentwing is somewhat similar to a dragonfly, but larger. Sometimes it seems to have two wings, other times four, or more, or none. Likewise, its color shifts from moment to moment. When it flies, it leaves silver seams in space that resemble quickly fading scars. And that's what Aeon Priests say these creatures are: transdimensional scars. Jacentwings are individually minor, but a swarm of them is a threat to other creatures and reality itself.

Motive: Hungers for transdimensional energy

Environment: Almost anywhere

Health: 3

Damage Inflicted: 1 point

Movement: Immediate when flying

Modifications: Speed defense as level 3 due to size

Combat: Jacentwings inflict 1 point of damage with their sting. If a swarm of five or more jacentwings attacks a single target, treat the swarm as a level 3 creature that inflicts 3 points of damage. Victims of a swarm attack must also succeed on a Might defense task or suffer one of the following additional effects.

1	Target is shunted to a pocket dimension until they can escape.
2	Crystal version of the PC pops out of a parallel dimension and falls on the real character.
3	The character's armor, clothing, piece of equipment, or entire pack is shunted to a pocket dimension.
4	A doppelganger of the character appears from an alternate dimension for a few rounds.
5	Target's hand or foot becomes lodged in an alternate dimension, and they may lose it unless they succeed on a difficulty 3 Might task.
6	The character's armor is damaged during the transfer to a pocket dimension as it becomes partly phased, reducing its Armor value by 1 until it can be brought "into tune" with the new dimension or until the PCs return to their home dimension.
7	One or more alternate dimensions begins to bleed through reality in the area around the character, increasing the difficulty of all tasks by one step for about a minute.
8	Target is shunted into a pocket dimension until they can escape. Each round in the pocket dimension is one hour in reality.
9	Transdimensional leeches (level 1) appear all over the target, as if they've always been there but just out of phase.
10	One of the target's cyphers is charged with transdimensional energy and explodes, inflicting damage equal to the cypher level to the target.

Interaction: Jacentwings act like insects but are drawn to items charged with transdimensional energy.

Use: Characters looking to travel the dimensions might seek a jacentwing hive.

Loot: If a character eats a jacentwing, mentally focuses on an alternate dimension, and succeeds on a difficulty 5 Intellect-based task, the PC is shunted to that dimension (which they must know to exist). If the jacentwing is alive, the difficulty is reduced by a step.

GM Intrusion: *Eating a jacentwing makes the character hallucinate and sick to their stomach for several hours on a failed difficulty 5 Might defense task.*

JASMERIS 5 (15)

These wide-faced flowerlike plants have bright scarlet petals and smell wonderful. They stand about 6 feet (2 m) tall but are not rooted. A jasmeris stalk is thick and robust, with many thick leaves that come to a point bearing wicked thorns. Even when the wind doesn't blow, the leaves and petals tremble in a way that many creatures find enticing, or at least deserving of closer examination.

Observers who get too close and stare into the flower's whorled and perfumed face are overcome by the invasive odor. The scent triggers a reaction, causing the victim's body to turn against itself. Victims begin to bleed internally until they completely liquefy. The resultant fluid is quite nutritious to a jasmeris.

Motive: Hungers for flesh

Environment: Anywhere plants can grow

Health: 20

Damage Inflicted: 5 points

Movement: Short

Combat: A jasmeris attacks targets with its barbed leaves, though its perfume is its most lethal quality. Unless the jasmeris's petals are folded, viewers within short range must succeed on a Might defense task or descend one step on the damage track each round. A creature that descends to the final step on the damage track because of this effect collapses into so much bloody liquid as the tiny cells making them up dissolve. This scent-triggered hemophilia occurs regardless of any other action—or attacks—the jasmeris takes.

To avoid this effect, a character within short distance must hold their breath. Holding one's breath in combat requires that a character succeed on a Might task each round. The difficulty begins at 1 and increases by 1 each round.

Some jasmerises have poisoned barbs, which means a victim hit with a leaf must also succeed on a Might defense task or suffer 2 points of Speed damage (ignores Armor) and be forced to take a big breath (if they were holding their breath).

Interaction: Jasmerises aren't intelligent, but they are as smart as an animal predator.

Use: The weird seeds sprout and begin to grow pretty red flowers, with thick leaves that almost seem to be forming barbs on the tips.

Loot: The valuables of past victims are found near jasmeris flower beds, including equipment, shins, and sometimes a few cyphers.

GM Intrusion: *The bones or equipment of a past victim snags the character's foot, which risks the PC falling over and inadvertently taking a breath on a failed difficulty 4 Might defense task.*

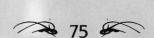

JREET   3 (9)

"Jreet?" The distinctive call of a jreet sounds almost comical, with its plaintive, questioning tone. But when a chorus of answering calls rises up around the listener, the comical quality rapidly gives way to the seriousness of the situation. Jreets are vicious, pack-hunting predators that coordinate their hunts with sound.

When prey is surrounded, a pack of jreets rushes from the underbrush or long grass, revealing their grotesque, elongated, 6-foot (2 m) long bodies. A jreet's forward-canted protuberance that is its head is given over to a series of separate mouths. Counterbalancing the head is a thick elongated tail tipped with a stinger. A nest of wiry limbs allows a jreet to run, climb, and burrow.

Many jreets sport scarification stripes and crude symbols, which might denote rank or something else within a given pack.

Motive: Hungers for flesh

Environment: Hunting plains and woods, usually in packs of five or more

Health: 12

Damage Inflicted: 3 points

Movement: Long; short when climbing; immediate when burrowing

Modifications: Perception as level 5; Speed defense as level 4 due to quickness.

Combat: A jreet attacks with its multiple-mouthed bite, inflicting 3 points of damage. A bite victim must also succeed on a Might defense task to pull free or be latched onto by the jreet's wiry limbs and suffer an additional 3 points of damage each round until escaping.

A pack of five or more jreets can act as a single level 5 creature and make a stampede attack. When they do, the pack moves 50 feet (15 m) in a round, and everything along the line of that movement is attacked. Victims take 5 points of damage, and even those who succeed on a Speed defense roll take 2 points of damage.

Finally, a jreet can use its poisoned sting against well-armored foes. The sting inflicts only 1 point of damage, but a victim must also succeed on a Might defense task or suffer 3 points of Speed damage (ignores Armor) each round for three rounds.

Interaction: Jreets are clever, predatory animals with highly developed social bonds that keep pack members close and cooperative.

Use: Any trip across the plains could involve a hunting pack of jreets.

Loot: A jreet pack burrow contains bones and sometimes equipment from previous prey that could include a few cyphers, 2d20 shins, and a few oddities.

GM Intrusion: The character hit by a poisoned jreet stinger doesn't take damage but instead falls into a hallucinogenic trance that lasts a few hours. During this period, the character is dazed and the difficulty of all tasks is increased by one step. However, after the episode passes, the PC has +1 to their Intellect Pool for the next couple of days.

JYBRIL 5 (15)

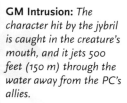

The jybril is a sea predator that routinely reaches 16 feet (5 m) in length whose flesh is infused with nanomachines that give it a truly unfair advantage over its prey. These sharklike creatures, with their massive mouths and complex eyes, are feared by land dwellers who go out to sea and by intelligent creatures of the deep, who sometimes call them "jawtails."

Jybrils eat anything, including humans, slimes, other predators of the deep, automatons, and other jybrils. Thanks to the nanomachines that infest jybril flesh, these creatures can digest anything and everything.

Motive: Hungers for flesh (or anything)

Environment: Almost anywhere underwater, hunting alone or in pairs

Health: 22

Damage Inflicted: 5 points

Armor: 1

Movement: Long when swimming; can "jet" 500 feet (150 m) through the water once per minute

Modifications: Perception as level 7.

Combat: A jybril can jet through the water at incredible speed for short bursts, which it does when attacking prey, especially prey that doesn't yet know it is being stalked. When using this jet attack, a jybril inflicts 2 additional points of damage. A jybril can make a jet attack about once every minute.

The nanomachines infusing jybril bodies provide the following additional benefits.

- +5 to Armor against damage from poison, venoms, or toxin.
- Regain 2 points of health each round.
- If the jybril does nothing other than drift with the current, the difficulty of its stealth tasks decreases by four steps until it moves or attacks.
- Once per hour (usually in conjunction with its first attack), it can release a pulse of energy that suppresses the active effects of cyphers and artifacts of the jybril's level or less for one round.

Interaction: Jybrils are predators and act that way.

Use: The PCs are hired by a nano to return with a living jybril so the nanomachines within its flesh can be studied. The nano gives them a map of a reef where jybrils are known to hunt.

Loot: Almost anything can be found in a jybril stomach, and a dead beast usually gives up 1d6 shins, one or two cyphers, and sometimes an artifact.

GM Intrusion: *The character hit by the jybril is caught in the creature's mouth, and it jets 500 feet (150 m) through the water away from the PC's allies.*

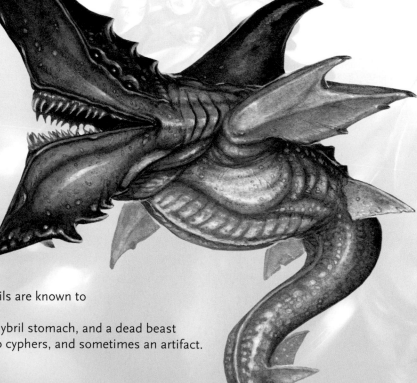

KAORUND 8 (24)

A deadly danger, infamous in the deep, the kaorund is gigantic, almost 80 feet (24 m) long, not counting the length of its tendrils. It hunts whales and similarly large prey, but is happy to attack almost anything. While it sticks mainly to the deepest parts of the sea, it's not unknown for one to come close enough to the surface to attack a ship. And of course, an entire submarine is fair game.

A kaorund has a long, spiny, snaky body, a number of tentacle arms, and a horrible mouth with powerful jaws.

Motive: Hungers for flesh

Environment: Anywhere in the ocean

Health: 75

Damage Inflicted: 10 or 8 points

Armor: 2

Movement: Long underwater

Modifications: Speed defense as level 6 due to size.

Combat: As a single action, a kaorund can attack with its bite, inflicting 10 points of damage, and attack two additional foes with its grasping tendril-arms for 8 points of damage. A foe grabbed by a tendril must succeed on a Might defense task or be grasped and pulled toward the kaorund's mouth, and in the next round the creature can use its bite to automatically inflict 10 points of damage.

But the kaorund has a different weapon in its arsenal as well. Instead of any of the previous attacks, it can lash out with two smaller tentacles near its mouth. Targets so much as touched by these get a bioelectric shock that stuns both biological and mechanical systems. Those failing a Might defense task cannot act for two rounds.

Last, if fighting a very large group, a kaorund can simply thrash about and attack all creatures within long range with the spines that cover its body. Each potential victim suffers 8 points of damage.

Interaction: There really is no peaceful interaction possible with a kaorund, a ravenous predator of animal intelligence.

Use: One of the scariest things in the sea, a kaorund is likely a challenge for an entire group of well-armed and well-protected characters. It's usually encountered far from a city or other such site.

GM Intrusion: *If the bitten character fails a Might defense task, they are swallowed alive by the kaorund. They can still attack the creature from within, but they suffer 10 points of damage each round while swallowed.*

KARESTREL   4 (12)

Karestrels are aggressive seabirds with a wide range and a fearlessness that makes them especially dangerous. That, plus their 20-foot (6 m) wingspans, vicious beaks, slashing talons, and ability to hunt equally well on land, in the air, and underwater.

Omnivores that nest in flocks and migrate between islands and icedrifts, karestrels spend most of their time overflying wave-tossed waters looking for prey. When they sense something, they flash downward into the chop with nary a splash, then emerge from the water seconds or minutes later with their prey grasped in cruel talons.

Motive: Hungers for flesh

Environment: Any cold climate in flocks of five to ten

Health: 19

Damage Inflicted: 4 points

Armor: 2

Movement: Short; long when flying or swimming

Modifications: Attacks as level 5; perceives as level 6; resists frightening effects as level 8.

Combat: Karestrels prefer to dive from the sky when they attack, and they usually gain surprise when flashing through the air and into the water to nab swimming prey. Attacks against surprised prey are modified by two steps in the attacker's favor. Their colorful wings provide more than physical armor and protection from cold (to which they are immune); karestrel plumage also bounces a blast of force, concentrated light, or a focused heat ray back in the direction it came from. Other kinds of energy are not redirected and affect the karestrel normally.

Some karestrels, when not in the water, emit a discombobulating hunting scream as part of their attack. The target must succeed on an Intellect defense task or the difficulty of its Speed defense task against the paired attack is increased by one step.

Interaction: Karestrels have animal-level intelligence. They are vicious, yet intelligent creatures sometimes rear and train karestrels. Commanding a trained karestrel is difficult (a level 6 task) but not impossible. A child or small person might even use a trained karestrel as a mount for a short time.

Use: A fishing boat drifts back to harbor under its own steam. The only bits of the crew that remain are bloodstains. In addition, the boat is scored as if with large talons, and many colorful feathers are found all over the ship, even within the forced-open inner crew compartments.

Loot: A karestrel nest, built high on a usually inaccessible rocky shelf, contains 2d6 shins, 1d6 cyphers, and possibly an artifact.

Surprise, page 95

GM Intrusion: *The character hit by the karestrel is carried a long distance straight up and then dropped, unless they succeed on a Might defense task to break free of the talons before they are carried upward more than an immediate distance.*

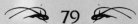

KASEYER — 3 (9)

Kaseyera are unstable abhuman predators with a hereditary psychosis so extreme that it grants the creatures dread mental abilities. Or perhaps the mental abilities are what produce the psychosis. It's difficult to know, and ultimately unimportant in the face of the threat a fresh kaseyer incursion represents.

Kaseyera are only somewhat humanoid, but they use their mental abilities to blend in with a local populace to cull prey. When the illusion falls away, a warped, spiny, sore-covered monstrosity stares through the tatters of the false image.

Motive: Hungers for flesh

Environment: Anywhere near human settlements

Health: 12

Damage Inflicted: 3 points

Armor: 1

Movement: Short

Modifications: Disguise and stealth as level 5.

Combat: A kaseyer can bite and claw a target, but it mostly relies on mental abilities. It uses those abilities not only to disguise its appearance (usually taking on the likeness of a human child or young adult), but also to assault the minds of victims. A kaseyer can trigger these abilities while alone, but prefers to work in mental concert with other kaseyera to increase the ferocity of the attack.

Brain Wrack: If a kaseyer touches a foe, the target must succeed on an Intellect defense task or be subject to a series of horrifying and shocking images that corrode the victim's brain, inflicting 3 points of Intellect damage (ignores Armor) and, on a failed Might defense task, stunning the victim so that they lose their next turn. If three or more kaseyera work as one to attack, the attack is a level 5 assault that inflicts 5 points of Intellect damage.

Sway: If a kaseyer touches a foe, it must succeed on an Intellect defense task or take an action specified by the kaseyer on its next turn. If three or more kaseyera work as one to attack, the attack is a level 5 assault.

Interaction: Kaseyera are mute, making no sound. They communicate telepathically among themselves, and instead of using direct telepathy with others, they prefer to use their ability to Sway to get other creatures to speak for them.

Use: A new gang of strangely quiet street urchins has appeared in the city of Auspar. Secretly, they're actually kaseyera.

Auspar, page 153

GM Intrusion: *The character subject to Brain Wrack remembers something about their past they'd forgotten, possibly something traumatic. Perhaps a past interaction with another entity with strong mental abilities made the PC forget.*

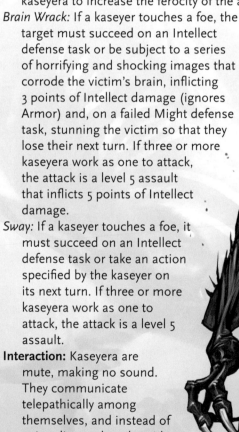

KEEPER   5 (15)

They look and act like normal people, almost. Usually, they're strangers. But they might be friends you've known for years. Like Talian the merchant who you've traded oddities with many times before. Something is different about her today. The woman standing at the cart evidences a faint trembling and hesitation to her actions you don't recall. A greenish moistness makes her skin shine. And when she speaks, even as she reminisces over shared past experiences, she takes a few moments before each response, almost as if she's reading from a script.

A keeper is a creature that steals humans and similar intelligent beings by covering them in (and filling them with) a thin film of liquid flesh. The victim remains alive and protected, but the keeper uses the victim's knowledge and skills to its own ends. Ends that vary by keeper—each is an individual motivated by its own desires.

Motive: Defense; depends on individual

Environment: Anywhere on the fringes of civilization

Health: 20

Damage Inflicted: 5 points

Armor: 3

Movement: Short (or as host body, if better)

Modifications: Knowledge skills as host body.

Combat: A stolen host body is almost completely protected by the keeper that has enveloped it, but it's also essentially in a state of stasis. Unless a keeper is damaged by an attack that affects everything in an area (such as a detonation, which affects both keeper and host), the host remains protected even as the keeper takes the brunt of any offensive.

A keeper can use any equipment or cyphers possessed by the host body, or it can exhale on a foe within immediate range. A target must succeed on a Might defense task or fall into a confused state. Until the target breaks free of the confusion with a successful Intellect task, it can take no other actions. If a keeper can maintain skin-to-skin contact with a confused victim for three rounds, it can transfer itself from the old host to the new host. The old host wakes within a few rounds, having moved down one step on the damage track. The new host falls unconscious, and the keeper regains any lost health.

Keepers with no host (a situation that rarely occurs) are a fluid gel that can move only an immediate distance each round on any surface.

Interaction: Keepers interact using their stolen host bodies. Some keepers may be partly motivated by memories discovered in their host, while others seek their own path.

Use: In order to survive a terrible event or situation, PCs may have to "protect" themselves using a synthetic gel manufactured by a strange device of the numenera.

A group known as the Twelfth Ode hunts and kills keepers whenever they hear hints of telltale activity.

GM Intrusion: *The host body is dispelled into a dangerous situation that must be dealt with or the unprotected body will die. The keeper uses the distraction to escape.*

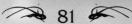

81

KELTONIM 3 (9)

Abhumans able to flit through the air can be dangerous, but the keltonim are even more deadly. When threatened, their bodies undergo a partial transformation that turns a sedate creature into a killer.

Keltonim are abhumans that build nests from salvaged synth and metal in high places, including along the tops of cliff faces and on the spires and towers of ruins. Simplistic and without a written language, keltonim are not generally considered dangerous. However, if personally threatened, they can call on a hidden reserve of fury that makes even the most stalwart glaive think twice about engaging them.

Motive: To be left alone

Environment: Anywhere high, often in groups of three to six

Health: 12

Damage Inflicted: 3 points (8 when transformed)

Movement: Short; long when flying

Modifications: When transformed, Speed defense and attacks as level 5.

Combat: Keltonim flee from combat unless they are hurt or a close ally is hurt. Then the fight-or-flight reflex is turned on its head as an ancient instruction hidden in keltonim flesh is activated over the course of one round, during which the creature does nothing but shake as if having a fit. If not killed or sedated before the beginning of its next turn, the keltonim is transformed for about a minute.

A transformed keltonim's muscles are taut beneath its skin, its eyes are wide, its mouth gapes, and wicked claws bloodily emerge from its fingers. A transformed keltonim inflicts an additional 5 points of damage (8 points total). A transformed keltonim cannot be stunned or dazed, and its skin thickens, providing +3 to Armor. Even when killed, a transformed keltonim usually gets a final death spasm attack.

Once a transformation runs its course, a surviving keltonim is dazed for several minutes, and all tasks it attempts are one step more difficult.

Interaction: Keltonim speak the local human language, but not very well. They are motivated by offers of food or a chance to avoid conflict. Most do not relish their transformation, despite the fact that the ferocity and violence of that transformation is what these abhumans are known for.

Use: Keltonim fill the "misunderstood creature" role well. Locals may have stories about a tribe of vicious, flying abhumans that prey upon them, when in fact the locals may be the ones antagonizing the abhumans in the first place.

Loot: Keltonim that lair in the high parts of prior-world ruins might carry a few shins and a cypher.

KELURSAN 7 (21)

Skinless, but rippling with muscle and embedded strands of machinery, a kelursan stands nearly 9 feet (3 m) tall. Red fluid constantly oozes from the creature, but inner healing technology keeps it hale and active, even in the face of killing environmental conditions or attacks from other kelursans. Thankfully, only a few handfuls of these creatures are active, and they mostly restrict themselves to out-of-the-way locations where they continually engage in their never-ending wargames, each against all the others.

Sometimes kelursans are damaged so severely that they suffer brain trauma and briefly forget their underlying imperative. These creatures wander into new lands, where they become either hunted monsters or lauded marvels, depending on how events play out. But sooner or later, as its healing factor finally concludes its work, a kelursan remembers, and returns to the "War Forevermore."

Motive: Defeat all other kelursans in the "War Forevermore"

Environment: Mountains, other empty places

Health: 30

Damage Inflicted: 8 points

Movement: Short; long when jumping

Modifications: Strength and Might defense tasks as level 8; Speed defense as level 5 due to size.

Combat: Kelursans batter their enemies with brutal ferocity. They can make a whirlwind attack targeting every creature within immediate range. In addition, they can hurl nearby boulders, chunks of synth, walls from ruins of the prior worlds, or other creatures at targets within long range, dealing damage to all creatures within immediate range of the impact zone that fail a Speed defense task.

Kelursans regain 4 points of health per round. If a kelursan inflicts damage during the same round in which its healing factor is active, it inflicts 2 additional points of damage (10 points total) with its attacks that round.

If a kelursan dies, embedded tech slowly reknits the creature, bringing it back to life within a few days unless the body is completely destroyed.

Interaction: A kelursan might know more languages than the one it shares with others of its kind. It isn't automatically hostile to characters, but it won't back down from even the hint of a fight. Once a kelursan begins to fight, it doesn't stop until it or its foes can't fight anymore.

Use: The strange being the PCs find helping children in a large city orphanage is actually a kelursan with a damaged memory.

Loot: A kelursan's remains can be salvaged for a couple of cyphers.

"War Forevermore" is what a kelursan says when it's defeated, or when it defeats another kelursan. It's an acknowledgement that whether victorious or defeated, kelursans always return to fight.

GM Intrusion: *The character hit by the kelursan must succeed on a Might defense task or be knocked back off the edge of a cliff or into another dangerous situation.*

KISSING FAWN — 3 (9)

Kissing fawns gambol across fields and wooded glades. Furred and slender, kissing fawns have large eyes, delicate necks, and several pairs of hooved feet. Humans might almost find them cute, except for the maggot-like wriggling mass of feelers that surrounds their mouths. Feelers occasionally drop off and slither away to hide under nearby rocks, fissures, or cracks in masonry. Kissing fawns also use these feelers to "kiss" their prey, a kiss that leaves a burning mark and several feelers behind writhing in the wound.

The feelers that drop off and don't burrow into living prey sometimes germinate in the ground, like seeds, and a plant grows over the course of a few weeks. These "kissing flowers" resemble a great sunflower with an animate stalk and a face that writhes with the same maggot-like feelers.

Motive: Reproduce

Environment: Anywhere

Health: 11

Damage Inflicted: 4 points

Movement: Short

Modifications: All tasks related to positive social interaction and deception as level 5.

Combat: A kissing fawn may seem playful as it runs about like a happy pet, even going so far as to "kiss" a target with its wriggling feelers. However, the corrosive slime produced by each feeler inflicts 4 points of damage, and if the target fails a Might defense task, a feeler detaches and burrows into the wound.

A target hosting one or more feelers finds the difficulty of all tasks one step higher due to the pain from the corrosive burrower, which also automatically inflicts 2 points of Speed damage (ignores Armor) each round until the target can extract it. Extracting a burrower usually requires some kind of tool that can be used as tongs, however crude, and inflicts 4 points of damage (ignores Armor) because of the trauma associated with the operation.

If a burrowing feeler kills a target, a new fawnling is born in the dead flesh, feeding on the body and growing until it finally emerges after about a week.

Interaction: Kissing fawns seem to understand simple commands in various languages, and they may even pretend to go along with directions or provide help. But it's all in an attempt to get potential victims to lower their guards.

Use: The traveling PCs discover a grove of strange "kissing flowers." Fallen forms, like sleeping (or dead) explorers, lie at the base of the grove.

Kissing flower: *level 3; moves an immediate distance each round; attacks as a kissing fawn*

GM Intrusion: *Hours after the characters have dealt with a kissing fawn, the PC notices that an ally bears a wound in which a tiny maggot is curled.*

KLAX 4 (12)

"The klax return every three years, buy up all the scrap synth and crystal available in Qi, and leave again. No one ever sees them arrive or depart, if you believe the stories. I don't. I'm going to discover their secret if it's the last thing I do."

~Cyntia, a nano

Floating through the air, ignoring gravity, a klax is humanoid with bluish skin and a tall, stretched head without hair, eyes, or nose, but with a very wide and expressive mouth. Stray discharges of electricity snap and pop between the ground and the flowing robes they wear that trail along the ground as they hover.

The klax apparently hail from some other world, or perhaps an alternate dimension. They refuse to speak of their origin and become defensive and angry if pressed. They are interested in broken oddities, used cyphers, and fragments of synth. They offer to pay with shins.

Motive: Accumulating scrap synth and used cyphers

Environment: Ruins and large cities

Health: 12

Damage Inflicted: 4+ points

Movement: Long when hovering

Modifications: Numenera knowledge as level 7.

Combat: A klax attacks with a touch that's charged with electricity. It can increase the intensity of the attack by sacrificing its own health, inflicting 2 additional points of damage per health point used. If a klax uses the last of its health to make an extremely powerful attack, instead of dying, it appears to fade away, falling back into whatever dimension, interstellar location, or time from which it projected itself. All their possessions go with them.

A klax can control a device of any size that is able to use power, as long as they remain in contact with it and the device is level 4 or lower. Each additional klax that touches the device increases the level of the device that can be controlled.

Interaction: Klax can speak the Truth and a few other languages with halting diction. They are usually unfailingly polite, even when facing aggressors, and prefer to offer a fair price for the goods they wish to purchase. If they feel wronged or cheated, they can become aggressive.

Use: An encounter with several klax merchants in a city can add interesting flavor, or be a central encounter if the klax somehow become angry with the PCs.

Loot: It's hard to loot a klax because they fade away when destroyed. But a klax usually carries a few oddities, 3d20 shins, and at least one or two working cyphers among many more used ones.

GM Intrusion: *Something the PC says or does makes the klax believe that the character is trying to cheat, lie, or steal from it, and it must be calmed to avoid an incident.*

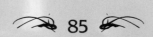

KROTH   4 (12)

The kroth is an 8-foot (2 m) tall amphibious creature that lives most of its life half covered in water. Its back, studded with irregular, protruding scales, can easily be mistaken for mossy rocks when the kroth lies partially submerged. Whoever tries to use those "rocks" as a path to cross the water becomes stuck, and the kroth rolls the victim under to drown it, then feed on it.

Motive: Hungers for flesh

Environment: Near water, alone or in groups of two or three

Health: 12

Damage Inflicted: 4 points

Armor: 3

Movement: Immediate; jumps a long distance

Modifications: Stealth and disguise as level 6; perception as level 3; Speed defense as level 3 due to size.

Combat: Kroth scales secrete a sticky fluid that bonds to most objects and surfaces, and that digests most materials. Characters who tread upon a kroth back must succeed on a difficulty 6 Might defense task or become stuck until they can escape.

Kroths that ensnare prey while lying submerged in water roll their prey beneath the surface. Attempting to "wrestle" a kroth while stuck to it in order to get a breath of air before being rolled under again requires a difficulty 5 Might-based task.

The adhesive, digestive fluid inflicts 4 points of damage per round to adhered victims, who may also be attempting to stave off drowning.

Interaction: Normally, no meaningful interaction is possible with a kroth. However, a few people have found kroth eggs and raised "tame" kroths to serve as guardians.

Use: Assassins or other enemies lead the PCs across a river where they know several kroths lie in wait. The foes avoid the stones that are kroth scales.

Loot: Possessions of former victims can be found in the water where a kroth has hunted. Searchers can usually pull 2d10 shins, a few oddities, and a cypher or two from the muck.

Drowning: For each three rounds a character goes with no air (as well as what is likely a few accidental breaths of water), they move one step down the damage track.

GM Intrusion: A character being rolled under the water must succeed on a difficulty 5 Speed defense task, or their head bashes into a submerged rock and they lose their next turn. In addition, they descend one step on the damage track as if they had gone three full rounds without a breath of air.

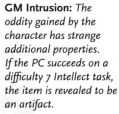

LACARIC COURIER 7 (21)

Lacaric couriers, for unknown reasons, deliver objects to distant locations, often near the ruins of some ancient city or structure. Occasionally, an explorer triggers a cypher or other strange device that summons a lacaric courier, which directly (or remotely) delivers an oddity, an artifact, or something else. Often, delivered objects have dangerous side effects and could be so unstable that any mishap causes them to detonate in a wide radius.

Lacaric couriers are wide, tall automatons with a variety of sphere-like extensions able to serve as limbs. The extensions also can open to reveal strange objects or the business ends of dangerous weapons.

The couriers occasionally make their deliveries using vast vehicles that resemble a series of stubby towers laid end to end, gapped by several feet of air but still somehow connected. The vehicle exterior changes from hour to hour or even moment to moment. Sometimes the surfaces resemble dark metal. Sometimes they're bright with complex patterns of light.

Motive: Deliver weird and dangerous objects for unknown reasons

Environment: Anywhere

Health: 33

Damage Inflicted: 7 points

Armor: 4

Movement: Short when flying; immediate when crawling

Modifications: Speed defense as level 4 due to size.

Combat: If threatened, a lacaric courier can direct up to four blasts of energy at the same or different targets within long range, or fire one blast of energy at a range of 1,000 feet (300 m) in lieu of making four attacks. If nothing else served, it could ram a target, inflicting 14 points of damage to both the target and itself, though its Armor applies. However, if attacked, a courier doesn't spend more than a few rounds defending itself.

Interaction: If not chased off or destroyed, a lacaric courier opens a sphere-like limb and ejects an object, which lands near a character. No other form of interaction has ever been achieved. The object is often a random oddity, but sometimes it's a useful artifact. In almost every case, artifacts possess a dangerous side effect determined by the GM, including slowly poisoning the user, infecting the user with an alien intelligence, and immediately detonating in a massive explosion.

Use: The characters activate an ancient machine, which seems to summon a lacaric courier.

Loot: A courier usually carries an artifact or a cypher.

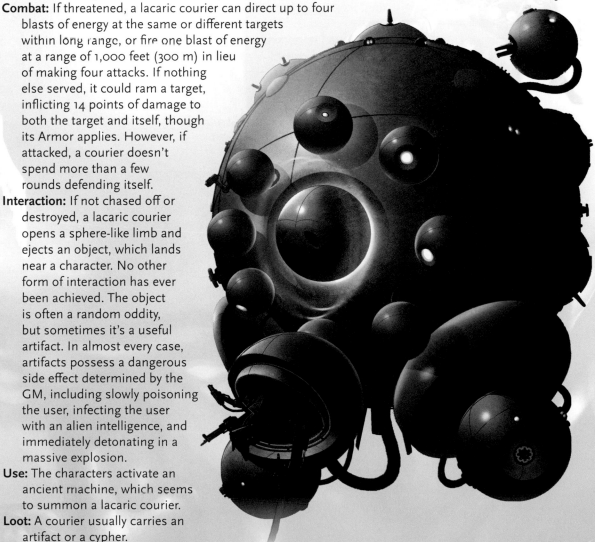

GM Intrusion: *The oddity gained by the character has strange additional properties. If the PC succeeds on a difficulty 7 Intellect task, the item is revealed to be an artifact.*

LAMBREQUIN 5 (15)

First impressions are important, and when a lambrequin is encountered, one probably gets the strong impression that these automatons care about nothing more than acquiring objects of the numenera and feeding on the energy. They can extend tentacle-like tendrils to suck the energy out of other machines nearby, and they don't seem all that picky whether or not such machines are simple tools or intelligent entities in their own right. This often leads to conflicts, but a lambrequin won't back off until satisfied.

A lambrequin is a little taller than a normal human. If a lambrequin is defeated, the automaton's remains are found to shelter a cavity in which a lumpy organic pod is growing and feeding on all the energy channeled to it by the lambrequin. The pod quickly dies when exposed to the elements and cut off from a steady supply of stolen energy.

Motive: Hungers for energy

Environment: Anywhere

Health: 20

Damage Inflicted: 5 points

Armor: 3

Movement: Short

Modifications: Tasks related to understanding and talking to machines as level 7.

Combat: A lambrequin can direct up to two blasts of energy at the same or different targets within long range, inflicting 5 points of damage.

As part of the same action, they can extend their head tendrils and attack all targets within immediate range or one target within short range. A character who fails a Speed defense task loses one cypher or oddity in their possession (in that order) as the tendril touches it and sucks away the energy. If the PC has an artifact, the character must check for depletion as some of the energy powering it is leeched away.

Each item a lambrequin sucks energy from grants it 3 points of health, even if that exceeds the creature's normal health maximum.

Interaction: A lambrequin knows many languages, and if contact is attempted, it might break off conflict if it has already consumed the energy of at least one item. It might leave characters be if they give it another cypher or two, and might even agree to help them if they agree to provide it with a steady source of energy. A lambrequin always refers to itself as "we" instead of "I" because it also refers to the entity it keeps armored and safe within.

Use: Always hungry for energy, lambrequins are fearless fighters, willing to seek out and attack targets with items of the numenera anywhere.

Loot: The remains of a lambrequin can be salvaged for 1d6 cyphers and one mysterious glob of organic matter that soon dies.

GM Intrusion: Instead of having its energy sucked out, the character's cypher explodes, inflicting damage (ignores Armor) equal to the cypher level to the PC.

LANMORO   4 (12)

Lanmoros have a psychic field that randomly triggers strong emotions in humans and similar creatures, such as hilarity when sober intensity is required, stabbing recollections of nostalgia, grief burning anew for a loss years in the past, and joy so strong it brings tears to the eyes. Lanmoros are creatures physically rooted in bubbling layers of greenish gel hidden in a crevice, crawlspace, cavity, or other non-obvious location. The gel forms different shapes, constantly flowing between images plucked from nearby minds.

Lanmoros feed on emotion by psychically triggering feelings in others. These feelings can vary wildly. For instance, a lanmoro's presence might provide the intensity of focus an artist requires to finish a project or a shy scholar to voice his love. But it could also make a normally placid woman want to kill her difficult and demanding older parent.

Motive: Hungers for emotion

Environment: Anyplace near where conscious minds congregate

Health: 12

Damage Inflicted: 4 points

Movement: Immediate

Modifications: Speed defense as level 2 due to slowness.

Combat: A lanmoro doesn't need line of sight to those it preys upon, only proximity (except when it uses its Bloom ability). A lanmoro can attempt any of the following attacks (or propagation methods) on its action.

Emotional Surge: A creature within short range must succeed on an Intellect task or be overcome with a strong emotion, such as sadness, hilarity, fear, disgust, or surprise. The target loses their next turn, or can attempt to wrench their mind back into focus, which inflicts 4 points of Intellect damage (ignores Armor) but allows the target to act normally.

Bland Grey Sky: Biological creatures with minds within short range must succeed on an Intellect defense task or lose all motivation for taking action for the next minute. Affected creatures pause and become unmoving, or perhaps slowly sink to the ground. A creature can attempt to escape this torpid state, but if successful, it suffers 4 points of Intellect damage (ignores Armor). Automatons are immune to this lanmoro ability.

Bloom: The lanmoro detonates and is destroyed. Creatures within immediate range and within line of sight must succeed on a Might defense task or suffer 4 points of damage. Over the next few days, juvenile lanmoros take root in random locations that exposed targets visit, usually in dark corners and behind shelves.

Interaction: Lanmoros don't seem intelligent, though they are highly emotional.

Use: A public house is infested with a strange new kind of "mold" that makes guests sometimes overly friendly and sometimes murderous.

Lanmoro specimens are occasionally captured and cultivated for the intensity of emotion they can instill. That's dangerous, because lanmoros have a way of spreading beyond their containment.

GM Intrusion: *When the emotion the character was feeling fades, the trauma is so significant that the PC must succeed on a level 4 Intellect task or fall one step on the damage track.*

LARUS 3 (9)

These abhumans have glistening beaked mouths, daggerlike claws, barb-studded shells, and burning green eyes. They groan with basso growls and can pull their limbs into their shells when faced by enemies. Larus live comfortably in deserts, near lakes, and even beneath the water in small air-filled cavities.

Like most abhumans, larus seem to delight in murder and sadistic acts against other creatures, but they take special pleasure in tormenting humans. Unlike many abhumans, larus are especially verbal and savor stories. They may stay their malice to hear a riddle or gripping tale, even if told by a foe. On the other hand, larus are consummate liars and enjoy promising victims mercy or help only to turn on them later, kill them, and serve them in great boiling pots as part of a feast for a larus community.

Motive: Hungers for flesh

Environment: Warm areas, sometimes near water, in groups of eight or more

Health: 9

Damage Inflicted: 3 points

Armor: 2

Movement: Short; short when swimming

Modifications: Deception as level 5.

Combat: Larus prefer to enter combat only by ambush. An ambush usually includes tunnels with flooded sections set with snares and nets designed to catch and drown. A larus can operate underwater for at least thirty minutes before it needs to draw a breath. A larus bite inflicts 3 points of damage, and its spittle injects a mild sedative that acts like venom; on a failed Might defense task, a victim is dazed for about a minute and finds the difficulty of all tasks increased by one step. Some larus use slings and (if any can be found) even cyphers.

When a larus would take enough damage to kill it, the creature instead instantly retracts its head and limbs into its shell, taking only 1 point of damage instead (which might still kill it, if it had only 1 point of health). On its next turn, it emerges again and acts normally. A larus can instantly retract about once per hour, which means larus that avoid death once are more likely to scuttle away than to keep fighting.

Interaction: Larus speak their own language, but some know the Truth. They are mad for stories and put off hostilities indefinitely while stories or riddles are being offered.

Use: A fishing village is being raided on an almost nightly basis by larus, which come not only for fish but also children, presumably to eat.

GM Intrusion: *The larus poses a riddle to a snared PC. If the PC can solve it, the larus promises to let the character go.*

LATOS ADJUNCT   5 (15)

These humanoid automatons possess a body composed of a strange alloy and a transparent sphere for a head. Within the sphere is a misty face, one that each viewer recognizes as their own.

Adjuncts are sometimes seen in proximity to far more noticeable figures called latoses that are 50 feet (15 m) tall. A latos sports a transparent sphere for a head that apparently contains a place of ancient importance, permanently preserved and deserted.

Adjuncts seem to act sometimes like latos herders and defenders, other times like servants sent out to gather specimens for study.

Motive: Protection
Environment: Deep wilderness
Health: 25
Damage Inflicted: 6 points
Armor: 3
Movement: Short
Combat: A latos adjunct can physically attack by battering foes with metal alloy fists.

Alternatively, it can lash out with horrific mental attacks. Attacks include the following:

All creatures within immediate range of the adjunct must succeed on an Intellect defense task or suffer 3 points of Intellect damage (ignores Armor).

One creature within short range of the adjunct must succeed on an Intellect defense task or their consciousness is transferred into the adjunct, where it can observe but not take any actions. Meanwhile, the adjunct controls the target's body, taking over so seamlessly that allies might not notice. Usually, it tries to convince the target's allies to leave the area, to ignore the latos, and so on. If necessary, the adjunct will attack the target's allies using the target's body. The adjunct can continue to act on its own even while it controls a target. The target can attempt to escape once per minute, and regains control of their body if they succeed on an Intellect task.

Interaction: An adjunct communicates telepathically. As latos caretakers, adjuncts sometimes are the key to providing characters with access to an ancient location the latos protects.

Use: A strange creature with a metallic body and a head enclosed in a clouded sphere enters the city. It asks about the characters because it wants a piece of the numenera they acquired during a recent adventure for purposes of its own.

Loot: Salvage from a destroyed adjunct yields an oddity, a couple of cyphers, and possibly an artifact.

Latos: level 10; for more information, see page 74 of The Ninth World Bestiary

GM Intrusion: The adjunct calls for a latos, which responds within a few minutes to a few hours, depending on how distant it is. The latos may be tasked to attack the characters or, more rarely, to give them access to the site it protects.

LERADYT   5 (15)

Quick and vicious, leradyts are a growing danger to isolated villages and small communities in the Beyond. These nearly human-sized carnivores run on dozens of scaled, clawed legs. Their long wormlike body is covered with scales, which spiral away from a blunt, eyeless head that features a circular mouth from which a whitish drool froths.

A lone leradyt can be deadly for a traveler, but leradyts hunt in small teams of two or three, which allows these clever creatures to take on bigger prey or groups with good odds of success.

Motive: Hungers for flesh

Environment: Almost anywhere away from cities and large towns, alone or in groups of two or three

Health: 15

Damage Inflicted: 5 points

Armor: 1

Movement: Long

Modifications: Perception as level 6.

Combat: A leradyt acting as part of a group attempts to either chase a lone target into the jaws of an ambush, or lead a group of targets into an ambush. Leradyt attacks from ambush increase the difficulty of defending against them by two steps, and deal a total of 7 points of damage.

A standard leradyt bite inflicts 5 points of damage, and the target must succeed on a Might defense task or be blinded by a splash of white, sticky froth until they use an action wiping away the muck. If a leradyt hits a blind target, it can wrap the befuddled victim in its clawed legs and inflict 5 points of damage each round until the target can escape. A blind target finds any task requiring sight at least two steps more difficult, if not impossible.

Interaction: Leradyts are impressive pack hunters, but they do not possess a language. That said, they might be convinced to call off an attack if something precious to them is threatened, such as their eggs.

Use: While traveling in the wild, the characters become the target of a pack of leradyts, which employ hit-and-run guerilla tactics to wear the PCs down.

Leradyt spit is prized in some areas for its analgesic qualities. Sometimes village healers mount expeditions to bring in a leradyt corpse so they can obtain this fluid.

GM Intrusion: In addition to the Might defense task to avoid being blinded, the attacked character must succeed on a second Might defense task to avoid becoming stuck in place until they can escape.

MACHINE EATER 3 (9)

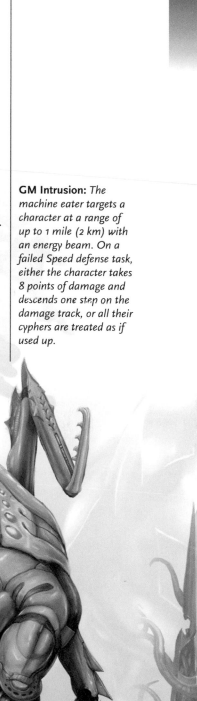

Machine eaters burrow vast tunnel complexes in solid structures, and are found both in the vastness of the night above the Earth, and here on Earth itself, especially near where craft and larger structures have fallen from the sky. To automatons and other forms of manufactured life, machine eaters are vicious and pernicious predators. To living creatures of flesh, machine eaters are not usually lethal, though they will go after any character who carries devices of the prior worlds. Machine eaters want to extract the power that many machines rely on to operate.

Machine eaters are void-adapted creatures, but they can operate in atmospheres and gravity just as well.

Motive: Hungers for devices of the numenera and automaton vital energy

Environment: Anywhere near or infesting structures and craft of the prior worlds

Health: 12

Damage Inflicted: 4 points

Armor: 1

Movement: Immediate; short when burrowing

Modifications: Perception as level 8 for detecting automatons, machine creatures, and creatures bearing cyphers and artifacts.

Combat: A machine eater clamps its sticky pedipalps onto its target, inflicting 4 points of damage. Against automatons and biomechanical creatures, that damage ignores Armor.

Instead of dealing damage, a machine eater can choose to drain an oddity, an artifact, or a cypher carried by the target. When this occurs, the item becomes useless, and the machine eater regains a number of points of health equal to the level of the drained object (treat oddities as level 1).

A machine eater can also attempt to stun automatons and biomechanical creatures within short range by generating a pulse of energy. Affected targets lose their next round of action, and artifacts and cyphers cannot be used for one round.

Interaction: Machine eaters are not sapient creatures; they are closer to burrowing vermin on Earth, though with a more predatory bent.

Use: A meteorite struck a city in the Ninth World. Unfortunately, it was riddled with tunnels and contained a nest of machine eaters. Now the surviving creatures are moving out into the city and causing havoc by eating every technological device they come across.

Loot: 1d6 cyphers (each one level higher than normal, up to a maximum of level 10) can be salvaged from a machine eater's deactivated form.

GM Intrusion: *The machine eater targets a character at a range of up to 1 mile (2 km) with an energy beam. On a failed Speed defense task, either the character takes 8 points of damage and descends one step on the damage track, or all their cyphers are treated as if used up.*

The planet of Urvanas is the second child of the sun. The creatures there seem simultaneously alien and familiar to human eyes.

MALORK   4 (12)

With the malorks' brown-hued hides, diaphanous wings, and penchant for gliding for long minutes, it's hard for their prey to distinguish these predators from the cloud banks and thunderheads that serve as their hunting ground far above the surface of the storm-swaddled planet of Urvanas. That is, until a malork gives voice to its supersonic screech, a noise so terrible that it splits atoms and rends flesh.

Some malorks have found their way to the skies high above the Ninth World.

Motive: Hungers for flesh

Environment: Alone or in groups of two or three. Some malorks are used as combat mounts by raiders.

Health: 24

Damage Inflicted: 5 points

Movement: Long

Modifications: Speed defense as level 3 due to size; tasks related to flying maneuvers and stealth while gliding near the cloud layer as level 5.

Combat: A malork tries to incapacitate prey from a distance with a long-range sonic blast that can target either a single creature for 5 points of damage, or all creatures in immediate range of a chosen spot for 3 points of damage. Creatures that take damage from the sonic screech must also make a secondary Might defense roll or be stunned for one round and unable to take actions. For flying creatures, this usually means loss of flight.

Up close, a malork's bite is almost as dangerous as its hunting cry.

A malork is adept at diving because it must often catch falling prey on the wing, but more important, it's skilled at pulling out of dives, even after entering the cloud layer. When a malork dives into a cloud, it usually emerges again in a place where the prey least expects it. The first time a malork surprises prey with this tactic, it gains an asset on its next attack on that target.

Interaction: Malorks are valued as mounts, but only after they've been broken and trained. Otherwise, they react like predators interested in eating and defending themselves.

Use: A malork nest of unusual size infests a floating ruin—a cloud city—that drifts with naturally occurring cloud banks. Either the nest needs to be burned out, or the floating ruin needs to be dropped.

Loot: Malork wing segments are crystalline in nature and sell for up to 20 shins per pane in a city.

GM Intrusion: The malork jostles or knocks the character off balance, and they fall unless they succeed on a difficulty 3 Speed defense task.

MALVOK   3 (9)

These sinuous, scaled abhumans have spiderlike limbs instead of arms and legs, and their faces are horrors of specialized mouthparts designed to puncture flesh and suck out a victim's insides. They hunt by stealth, burrowing up through rock and structures with careful, quiet precision until they find someone sleeping in a bed or bedroll, whereupon they quickly kill and sup on a victim's interior while hardly disturbing the victim's pose. Companions in the same structure or camp as a malvok victim might not even realize their friend is dead, and merely assume they are still sleeping. At least until they shake the victim and discover the flaccid, collapsed flesh, the gaping hole in their back, and the excavated, blood-drenched cavity in the sleeping surface beneath them.

Malvoks don't have leaders; the small hunting groups communicate by voice, making low, thrumming, gurgling sounds in the back of their throat. While they can subsist on most any flesh, they are particularly drawn to eating humans, as if addicted.

Motive: Hungers for flesh, especially that of humans

Environment: Malvoks hunt in small groups of three to six under human communities and cities

Health: 12

Damage Inflicted: 3 points

Armor: 2

Movement: Short; immediate when burrowing

Modifications: Defends as level 4 due to slick scales; stealth tasks as level 6 when burrowing.

Combat: If caught, malvoks might use crude weapons like spears or clubs to defend themselves before they attempt to slip away down a freshly burrowed hole in the ground. They avoid open conflict when possible, and instead try to skewer sleeping (or at least reclining) foes from the safety of stealthily extended tunnels. Defending against a surprise bite by a malvok is two steps more difficult (or impossible for a sleeping target). A victim takes 3 points of damage and must succeed on a difficulty 5 Might defense task or be completely paralyzed and unable to take physical actions until the damage from the initial bite is restored.

A malvok secretly feeds on a paralyzed victim through the same puncture cavity it used to inject its paralytic venom, inflicting 3 points of damage (ignores Armor) each round as it sucks out the organs.

Interaction: Characters who catch malvoks in the act might be able to negotiate with them, because for all their hunger, the abhumans do not crave open conflict. But keeping a malvok ally means always sleeping with one eye open.

Use: The characters are asked to look into a series of "assassinations" in an upscale neighborhood that leaves the corpses mostly devoid of internal organs. A rival political faction is blamed because tensions are high.

GM Intrusion: A character who survives a malvok bite discovers tiny lumps under their skin a day later. Allergic reaction? Severe bruising? Eggs?

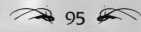

MAZOCACOTH
6 (18)

Only a few mazocacoths walk the Ninth World. They have two aspects, which vary by the sun's position. The aspect active at night is a massive, phased entity towering at least 300 feet (90 m) that has many legs, like a spider, allowing it to move nimbly across mountain ridges and desert ravines alike. This "darkwalker" aspect is translucent but has the faintest of bluish glows, rendering it visible to some as it moves silently overhead like a scudding cloud.

The aspect active by day is the collapsed and solid version of the creature. This "sleeper" aspect is only 5 feet (2 m) in diameter, has only two legs and an almost human face, and prefers to sleep if left alone, though it also spends a few hours browsing vegetation.

Many who've seen a darkwalker get the sense that it's looking for something, though probably something that hasn't existed for aeons. Never succeeding doesn't keep mazocacoths from the search.

Motive: Searching for something lost

Environment: Anywhere

Health: 22

Damage Inflicted: 8 points

Armor: 2 (in sleeper aspect)

Movement: Long in darkwalker aspect; short in sleeper aspect

Modifications: Perception as level 9.

Combat: A mazocacoth in its darkwalker aspect usually enters combat only if an attacker is able to affect its phased form, requiring a device designed to affect out-of-phase creatures or a weapon that relies on transdimensional energy. But if threatened, a darkwalker can extend one of its many legs to stab a foe within 300 feet (90 m), inflicting 8 points of Intellect damage (ignores Armor) to the target as well as to all targets within immediate range of the primary target who fail a Speed defense task. Those who succeed still suffer 2 points of Intellect damage (ignores Armor).

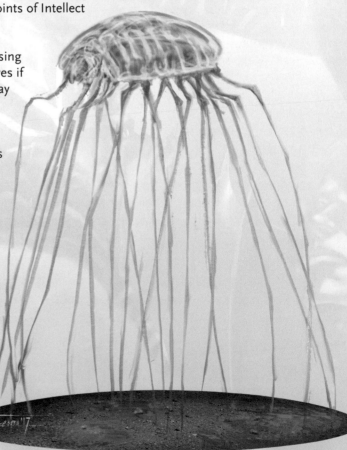

Sleeper mazocacoths that are roused from slumber or found while browsing vegetation do not defend themselves if attacked, though they do move away at full speed.

If a mazocacoth is killed in either aspect, a psychic cry inflicts 8 points of Intellect damage (ignores Armor) on all creatures within a mile (2 km) of the deed. The body fades away over the course of a few hours.

Interaction: A mazocacoth never speaks, but sometimes it grants boons to creatures that approach it respectfully, if they can get its attention.

Use: The PCs hear of a "night demon" that haunts a nearby mountain range. But locals in the area worship the nightly apparition as a god that, they say, keeps them safe from "real" demons that would otherwise spill up out of the earth.

In either form, the creature has access to a variety of additional abilities that include the power to heal creatures, teleport long distances, see several hours into the future, and probably more.

GM Intrusion: A squad of Oorgolian soldiers—and one Oorgolian tester—reveal themselves on a rise near the PCs as they fire a transdimensional weapon at a passing mazocacoth in its darkwalker aspect.

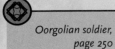

Oorgolian soldier, page 250

Oorgolian tester, page 120

MERCURIAL WASP   3 (9)

Aggressive. Angry. Voracious. Deadly. These are words you might use to describe a swarm of mercurial wasps, if their venom wasn't already closing your throat and paralyzing your vocal cords. These undersea wasps swarm through the water. The blue-and-black striped creatures—only about 1 foot (30 cm) long—might be small, but they're deadly. They appear to constantly shift between solid metal and liquid metal states, making them difficult to see, much less strike.

Mercurial wasps eat metal and build their hives by chewing complex tunnels and rooms deep inside structures. A hive can house as many as three dozen wasps.

Hidden and protected deep inside each hive is the Court, a group of three slightly larger wasps that are more clearly solid metal constructs. Unlike other mercurial wasps, members of the Court have large, glowing orange eyes and no visible stingers. They are able to communicate and might attempt to beg for mercy. They flee the hive rather than fight, should it come to that.

Motive: Territoriality

Environment: Underwater, near metal structures, vessels, and machines in groups of one to three dozen

Health: 9

Damage Inflicted: 4 points

Armor: 1

Movement: Long

Modifications: Defend as level 4 due to shifting states.

Combat: A character struck by a mercurial wasp's sting must succeed on a Might defense task or be paralyzed, unable to move, for one round.

A swarm of five mercurial wasps work together to attack with stunning speed and coordination as a level 5 creature, inflicting 8 points of damage, and the paralytic effect lasts for two rounds.

Interaction: Members of the Court may attempt to cajole or reason with the PCs if they feel threatened.

Use: Due to the wasps' proclivity for metal, they may attempt to build a hive in the PCs' vessel, or perhaps they've already established one among metal ruins that the characters are exploring.

Loot: A wasp's venom sac holds enough poison for three uses. The barb can be used as the blade of a shiv or other light weapon.

Mercurial hive: *level 7*

Member of the Court: *level 3, persuasion as level 4; health 20; Armor 4*

Paralysis, page 95

A swarm of a dozen mercurial wasps is a challenge for even powerful PCs. The GM can have a group of five wasps attack en masse as a single creature that is two levels higher, inflicting double the original creature's normal damage.

GM Intrusion: *The stung character is paralyzed for two rounds rather than one.*

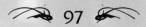

MIMUS 6 (18)

These hulking 10-foot (3 m) tall creatures are ropy with muscle and studded with glowing mechanical protrusions that flash intermittently. Often, a mimus settles into a location by burrowing most of its body underground or within a screen of structures or foliage. Their faces, however, seem almost human, which is usually what prey first sees. Human, at least, until the façade face splits open and peels back to reveal a horrific visage spewing leechlike projectiles at anyone that's moved too close. Spit leeches that land on a victim's flesh begin to burrow, heading for the prey's brain. Victims succumb while experiencing alien emotions and images. Are mimuses actually just trying to communicate?

Motive: Communicate by consuming minds of target creatures

Environment: Almost anywhere humans or other intelligent creatures frequent

Health: 22

Damage Inflicted: 6 points

Armor: 1

Movement: Short; immediate for burrowing or climbing

Modifications: Speed defense as level 4 due to size; stealth tasks as level 7 due to ability to hide most of its body.

Combat: A mimus hides in plain sight by digging in or hiding behind convenient structures so that only its head is visible. Such a peculiarity is enough to lure some victims to within immediate range. That's when the face splits and erupts with a shower of burrowing leeches. On a failed Speed defense task, targets suffer 6 points of damage and an additional 6 points of damage (ignores Armor) each round thereafter from burrowing leeches until they succeed on a Might-based task to expel the leeches. After a few rounds, victims begin to suffer flitting hallucinations and odd visions that make no apparent sense.

Interaction: The only way a mimus can communicate is by spitting up burrowing, brain-eating leeches. This is almost always lethal for a victim, though it's possible (barely) that some form of negotiation could occur before brain death.

Use: A new gang of thieves and bandits has come to the city. Those who cross the gang are captured and brought to see Empty Face, a fate rumored to be horrific. Empty Face is, in fact, a mimus.

Mimuses might be visitors from a bizarre dimension or remnants of a transdimensional civilization that once incorporated the world. It's hard to know for certain.

GM Intrusion: The character hit by leeches must succeed on an Intellect defense task or be overcome by strange visions. The victim loses their next action. However, the round after that, the leeches disengage, fall out of the wounds, and die, while the character learns a secret chosen by the GM.

MNETHASHI   5 (15)

Arachnoid-humanoid amalgams with cruel claws, mnethashi may have extraterrestrial origins, but their kind has dwelled on Earth for as long as the Ninth World has existed (and probably much longer). As they cannot abide the sun, mnethashi dwell underground in militaristic societies dominated by strength and the capacity for cruelty and betrayal. Although there are exceptions, the mnethashi see humanity as something to be conquered and enslaved.

A mnethashi stands about 5 feet (2 m) tall.

Motive: Domination

Environment: Anywhere, often in the company of enslaved humans or other creatures

Health: 18

Damage Inflicted: 8 points

Movement: Short

Modifications: Stealth and deception as level 7.

Combat: Mnethashi claws drip with a powerful acid that also runs through their blood. The damage they inflict includes 3 points of acid damage. Further, if they are struck in melee, the creature striking them suffers 2 points of acid damage from the blood spray.

Mnethashi are experts in stealth. Beyond moving quietly and slipping into shadows, they can cloud the minds of other creatures, implanting confusing or false images. Those failing an Intellect defense task cannot help but be confused by or even believe in these psychic illusions.

Mnethashi have mental powers that they can use offensively as well. A target within short range that fails an Intellect defense task suffers 6 points of Intellect damage (ignores Armor). A character reduced to 0 Intellect in this way loses much of their will and obeys any command or suggestion sent to them telepathically. This condition lasts until their Intellect Pool is completely restored.

Mnethashi often use cyphers or artifacts, usually as weapons.

Interaction: Mnethashi can speak telepathically to anyone (and, if they wish, everyone) within long range. Further, they can read the basic surface thoughts of anyone within short range, even if the target is unwilling. They are excellent liars and have learned exactly how to best influence and manipulate humans.

Use: A small cadre of mnethashi assassins has been dispatched by the characters' enemies to find and eliminate them.

Loot: A mnethashi typically carries a cypher or two, and perhaps an oddity.

Mnethashi use their powers to ensure that their slaves never fully restore their Intellect Pools.

GM Intrusion: *The mnethashi disappears into the shadows immediately after making its attack. The characters have no idea where it is.*

MOILT

The many-eyed moilt shambles on a tangle of thrashing tendrils, emerging from hollows in the ruins of prior worlds where it takes shelter. Its bloated white body has a bread-like texture that smells of esoteric spice. When it finds lone humans and other creatures of equivalent or greater intelligence, it locks gazes and inserts a psychic compulsion. Those who succumb to the impulse are drawn to the moilt, and the creature offers up the flesh of its body for a few hearty bites. This damages the moilt, but not usually fatally.

Those who eat of moilt flesh are poisoned, and drop unconscious. Those who survive wake with a fragment of memory, vision, or sensation that is usually wholly incomprehensible and often traumatic until it can be forgotten.

Motive: Offer its flesh for food to intelligent creatures

Environment: Almost anywhere near ruins

Health: 24

Damage Inflicted: 2 points

Movement: Short

Combat: Moilts don't usually fight in the physical sense, but they can use their tangle of tendrils to attack all creatures within immediate range for 2 points of damage as a single action.

Moilts prefer to hypnotize creatures with their psychic gaze if threatened. A moilt can potentially mentally affect all creatures that meet its gaze within short range as one action. Affected creatures that are not at least as smart as humans forget that the moilt is present.

A human or equivalently intelligent creature is compelled to move forward and take a few bites from the moilt's soft, bread-like outer flesh (which inflicts 1 point of damage to the moilt). Upon swallowing, the diner must succeed on a Might defense task or fall unconscious for about an hour. Unless awakened prematurely, those who eat of the moilt wake with a new memory, which is usually so out of context that little can be gleaned from it.

Interaction: Moilts don't seem to be self-aware or intelligent, though they are sly when it comes to finding new targets to whom they offer up their flesh.

Use: A village keeps a moilt prisoner and uses it as part of a strange ritual where participants gain visions of strange and distant places. Every so often, a participant has a bad reaction to the imparted vision, but that's considered a reasonable sacrifice by those unaffected.

GM Intrusion: The character who wakes with a memory imparted by a moilt discovers something actionable about it; they can use the information to access a secret, discover a buried ruin, activate an ancient craft, and so on.

MORIGO 6 (18)

Morigo are biomechanical remnants of a prior age, likely created by bioengineers with great knowledge and skill. Although no more intelligent than the other fish they hunt, they come equipped with advanced technological systems that give them clear advantages.

Morigo are extraordinarily agile swimmers, possessing biomechanical sensors that allow them to sense movement, pressure changes, temperature changes, and more with incredible accuracy.

Motive: Hungers for flesh

Environment: Anywhere in the ocean

Health: 26

Damage Inflicted: 6 points

Armor: 2

Movement: Long underwater

Modifications: Perception as level 8; swim as level 7.

Combat: As an action, a morigo can generate a pulse of infrasound that reverberates through the water, affecting all in long range. A morigo has a number of hovering pods around it, each of which functions to amplify and direct the waves of infrasound. Victims in the area failing an Intellect defense task have their mind affected by the infrasound in a randomly determined fashion:

01–30	Dazed for one round—the difficulty of all actions is increased by one step
31–40	Stunned for one round—no action
41–45	Utter immobility for one round
46–55	Panic for one round, during which the character moves away at top speed
56–70	2 points of Intellect damage and dazed (as above) until those points are restored
71–80	3 points of Intellect damage and dazed (as above) until those points are restored
81–90	4 points of Intellect damage and dazed (as above) until those points are restored
91–00	Madness for one round, during which the character attacks nearest target

Morigo bite those affected by their pulse. They are immune to infrasound effects.

Interaction: Morigo are sly but have only animal intelligence.

Use: Morigo are nasty predators, using their infrasound attack to disable whole groups and then moving in to attack the choicest target. They are fearsome alone, but deadly when encountered in a pack.

Loot: A morigo is a biomechanical creature, and knowledgeable characters can scavenge a random cypher and an oddity from its corpse.

GM Intrusion: The infrasound pulse triggers the character's artifact or cypher in an unexpected fashion.

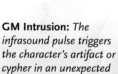

MOZCK AUTOMATON 5 (15)

The entity called Mozck is a machine intelligence with no apparent physical form. Instead, Mozck flits from servitor drone to ancient machine to artifact and on to some other mechanism by compromising and overriding the previous controlling consciousness. After Mozck has overwritten an automaton, the compromised entity gains hideous new abilities and becomes sociopathic, twisted, and what can only be described as evil. Why else would a Mozck automaton inflict such terrible, spirit-wracking transformations on its victims? One thing is clear, if nothing else: Mozck understands the numenera far better than almost any other entity.

More powerful instantiations of Mozck likely exist, running the gamut all the way up to a level 10 nanoswarm creature of ever-shifting shape and abilities.

When an instantiation of Mozck infiltrates and overwrites a machine, it changes its outward appearance over time until it resembles a nightmare machine version of a scorpion, a starfish, and a weapon.

Motive: Inscrutable

Environment: Almost anywhere on or near Earth

Health: 20

Damage Inflicted: 5 points

Armor: 3

Movement: Short

Modifications: Tasks related to understanding and manipulating the numenera as level 10; detecting falsehoods as level 7.

Combat: A Mozck automaton makes physical attacks with a bladed wing, pincer, tentacle tip, or some other implement related to its form. However, a mature Mozck automaton (one that's fully transformed, which takes a few days) usually relies on psychic attacks that disrupt the thought processes of organic and machine intelligences. A target within long range must succeed on an Intellect defense task; on a failure it takes 5 points of Intellect damage, and the difficulty of its actions is increased by one step while it remains within long range of the Mozck automaton.

A target that is defeated by a Mozck automaton may be killed, though some survive. Those that do are infected with a nanoscopic parasite that slowly begins to change their flesh in random and usually horrible ways (if desired, the GM can refer to the Harmful Mutations list).

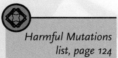

Harmful Mutations list, page 124

Most Mozck automatons regain health at a rate of 1 point per hour, even when they are at 0 health. The only way to eliminate this ability is to destroy the automaton utterly.

Interaction: If a Mozck automaton communicates at all, it usually does so in broken psychic images that tend to nauseate humans and rarely offer any real chance of negotiation.

Use: These compromised machines can be found in many ruined installations, just waiting for a powered device to come along to activate it after who knows how many millennia of sleep.

GM Intrusion: The automaton uses its psychic ability to anticipate and negate the character's attack(s) for one round.

Loot: The inactive (though slowly regenerating) remains of a defeated Mozck automaton can be salvaged for 2d6 shins and 1d6 cyphers.

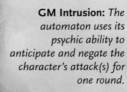

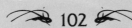

MUJIDAVAR   6 (18)

The universe is an interesting place. It contains location of incredible beauty. But it's also home to a predatory terror with a hideous countenance known as a mujidavar. Mujidavari were first encountered on an artificial world well beyond the reaches of Earth's galaxy. Somehow, some of these creatures have found their way to the Ninth World.

   Mujidavari are bipedal, scaly monstrosities with long tails. Where one might expect a head, a mujidavar has a squirming mass of tendrils and tiny mouths. Some of the tendrils end in bony blades, some in bulbous eyes, and a few in still more tiny mouths.

Motive: Hungers for flesh

Environment: Distant locations in the void or anywhere on Earth with a connection to locations in the void

Health: 28

Damage Inflicted: 6 points

Armor: 3

Movement: Long

Modifications: Stealth and Speed defense as level 4.

Combat: A mujidavar can use an action to move a short distance and then attack with its tendrils or use its subsonic screech. Despite having a large number of tendrils, the creature can use them to attack only a single foe at a time.

The terrible focused screech of a mujidavar operates on a subsonic level, which can scramble the senses of a single foe within short range. If the target fails an Intellect defense roll, they believe that everything they see and hear is not precisely where it truly is. As a result, the difficulty is increased by three steps for attacks, Speed defense rolls, movements, or tasks involving targeting or knowing where something is.

Interaction: The mujidavar is basically an animal—a belligerent, predatory animal.

Use: A pair of mujidavari is terrorizing a small, isolated community, and the PCs traveling by are the villagers' only hope. As a reward, they offer the characters the location of a cache of cyphers or similar items.

GM Intrusion: *The character is caught in the tendrils of the mujidavar and cannot move unless they succeed on a Might-based task. In each round that they remain caught, they suffer damage as the creature automatically bites them.*

MULTROLCA 7 (21)

Multrolcas are rare specimens, bred for war in a prior world, wounded and gone to ground for years uncounted. A multrolca is a 20-foot (6 m) long nightmarish beast of claws; jutting, glowing devices of the numenera; silvery fur; and seeping blood from gashes that never seem to heal.

A multrolca seems drawn to barren places to sleep, but once disturbed, a rage kindles in it that compels it to roam widely, visiting destruction and death on whatever it encounters until its wounds force it back into hidden convalescence.

A multrolca convalescence period lasts anywhere from a week to several years.

Abhuman tribes in the area where a multrolca wakes either clear out or revere the creature as a manifestation of savage divinity. They ply it with sacrifices of prisoners taken from other tribes or, better yet, captive humans.

Motive: Destruction

Environment: Barren and mountainous locations

Health: 32

Damage Inflicted: 10 points

Armor: 3

Movement: Short; short when climbing

Modifications: Speed defense as level 6 due to size.

Combat: A multrolca chases prey with single-minded intensity, bounding from boulder to cliff wall, slavering and roaring with horrendous fury. The multrolca's bite inflicts 10 points of damage, and if the victim fails a Might defense task, venom inflicts an additional 6 points of Speed damage (ignores Armor).

A multrolca that commits itself to combat begins to bleed from ancient wounds after a few rounds of activity, which inflicts 1 point of damage per round to the creature. These re-opened wounds eventually become life threatening; at that point, the multrolca activates the strange devices studding its skin, opens a temporary wormhole to another location, and attempts to escape to safely and convalescence.

GM Intrusion: *The savagery of the multrolca's initial attack takes the character by surprise, causing the PC to lose their first turn unless they can succeed on an Intellect defense task.*

Interaction: A multrolca is intelligent and able to communicate but rarely shows this quality while hunting or attacking. A convalescing multrolca is willing to negotiate, whereupon it expresses a profound sadness at its unending life and unquenchable rage that will inevitably ignite again.

Use: The characters stumble across a multrolca in the last few hours of its convalescence. It tries to warn them to get away before "everything changes."

Loot: A few cyphers and an artifact can be salvaged from a multrolca's remains.

NACREON WIND   2 (6)

A nacreon wind exists in two states, dispersed and concentrated. Those who witness a passing nacreon wind might not ever know that it's a living creature unless it moves from a dispersed state to a concentrated state. It mostly remains dispersed as a swirling collection of glowing white-blue motes. The motes swirl within an area at least a long distance in diameter. Most onlookers assume the phenomenon is merely weather. However, when it becomes agitated, it can concentrate its form, becoming a single glowing mass that mimics the form of the creature or object that triggered its interest.

Some explorers seek out passing nacreon winds, whether or not they know the wind is actually a creature, because they believe seeing them is a good omen. It means that objects of the numenera are likely to be close by. Such objects may spontaneously power on and reveal their presence thanks to an invisible resonance with the nacreon wind. This residual "feeding" usually satisfies the creature, but sometimes the wind forms a semisolid body to interact with the object.

Motive: Inexplicable

Environment: Anywhere

Health: 9

Damage Inflicted: 3 points

Movement: Short when flying

Combat: In its dispersed state, a nacreon wind is insubstantial. It can't be affected by anything unless the attack is transdimensional. The creature fills an area a long distance across, and it can move through small cracks and fissures. In this state, it cannot attack other creatures. Its presence in the area makes all tasks related to finding objects of the numenera one step less difficult, as those objects tend to gleam, power on, or otherwise reveal themselves as the glowing motes sip residual energy from them.

As an action, a nacreon wind can concentrate down to a fraction of its former size and become a solid that mimics, in outline only, the shape of a character or object. In this shape, it touches a character (who allows it, or who fails a Speed defense task) or unattended cypher and "rewrites" its functionality with a pulse of light. If this happens to a character, randomly choose one new cypher for that PC (the old cypher remains in form, but it has a new function).

If attacked, a concentrated nacreon wind is vulnerable to damage. It can also return an attack as a slap or jab, inflicting 3 points of Speed damage (ignores Armor) if the target fails a Speed defense task.

Interaction: This energy creature is somewhat inexplicable. Those in the know follow nacreon winds about, hoping to discover rich new caches of the numenera.

Use: An area along a windswept coast is known to be rich in the numenera as well as strange weather patterns that produce thousands of tiny motes of light.

GM Intrusion: *The cypher touched by the nacreon retains whatever capacity it had before, but it also gains a secret effect: if the cypher is activated, it summons a lacaric courier.*

Lacaric courier, page 87

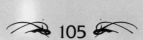

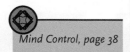

Mind Control, page 38

GM Intrusion: The character gains a memory so alien and inexplicable that their brains can't process it, and they must succeed on an Intellect defense task before they can take another turn.

NAMNESIS   5 (15)

A namnesis appears to be composed of silvery, liquid metal. When disturbed or after it becomes aware of other creatures, a namnesis takes the rough shape of the nearest intruder, sometimes splitting the difference between multiple intruders in a horrific fashion. A namnesis attempts to follow the creature (or creatures) it mimics.

A namnesis communicates by trading memories with targets it has mimicked. The target may realize they don't remember the town where they were born, who their parents were, or perhaps even their own name. Instead, brand-new memories have been inserted that are sometimes mundane, like the smell of a green flower growing in a meadow, and sometimes unbelievable, like the memory of a star going supernova.

Motive: Communicate

Environment: Almost anywhere

Health: 18

Damage Inflicted: 3 points (see Combat)

Armor: 3

Movement: Short

Combat: If threatened, a namnesis attempts to psychically remove a character's special ability and use it for itself. For instance, if a nano with the Mind Control esotery confronts a namnesis, the nano must succeed on an Intellect defense task or lose the use of that ability for about a minute. As part of the same action, the namnesis attempts to use Mind Control on the character or the character's ally. If a namnesis fails to "borrow" an ability, the target instead takes 3 points of Intellect damage (ignores Armor) that round.

A namnesis may also attempt to remove a foe's memory of their initial meeting so it can slip away or try again, though this works only against a single foe without allies.

Interaction: The memories a namnesis trades seem random, though PCs who are persistent might be able to gain specific memories from a namnesis that could aid them. A namnesis is intelligent and attempts to negotiate to gain access to new memories whenever possible.

Use: A corrupt noble or Aeon Priest uses a namnesis ally to sift victims of valuable memories, which they transfer to themselves.

NAUSRAK   2 (6)

Accumulations of toxic fungus, nausraks arise in some areas where invisible influence from broken devices of the numenera kills off normal life. A nausrak grows like a film of hardly visible microbes until it finally matures and animates like a creature. Animate nausraks are about 4 feet (1 m) tall, and they try to hide their fungal nature under stolen human clothes and equipment.

Most nausraks are concerned primarily with hiding their true form, because other creatures usually react poorly. Nausraks that remain in one area for too long risk infecting other living creatures with reproductive spores. Infected creatures eventually collapse, covered in strange orange fungus.

Motive: Hide their presence, reproduction

Environment: Anywhere near installations from the prior worlds, in groups of four to ten

Health: 9

Damage Inflicted: 3 points

Movement: Short

Modifications: Stealth and deception as level 5; resists poisons and passive energy attacks as level 8.

Combat: A nausrak attacks by scraping a glob of fungus from its body and hurling it at a foe. A struck target takes 3 points of damage from burrowing myofibrils in the glob and must also succeed on a Might defense task or become infected.

If three or more nausraks target a single foe, it's treated as a single level 5 attack that inflicts 8 points of damage, and the Might defense task to avoid becoming infected is difficulty 5.

An infected target chokes, struggles for breath, and loses their next turn. The infection is a level 5 disease. Every 28 hours after the spores take root, the victim must succeed on a Might defense task or descend one step on the damage track as an orange-colored fungus begins to grow on and in them, but especially over any objects of the numenera they carry. If a target completely divests itself of all such items for 56 hours, the infection is cured. If a victim dies while infected, their corpse (or pile of divested items of the numenera) is ground zero for a fresh nausrak infestation.

Interaction: Nausraks can learn to speak human languages and do so to try to hide their true nature. Nausraks usually prefer to stay with others of their kind, but one separated from others may ally with humans to gain aid.

Use: A band of "abhumans" is discovered living in the shadow of an old ruin. The abhumans have been stealing clothing and other equipment from a clave, but they don't seem violent. The clave hires the PCs to parley with the creatures to see if they can come to terms and end the midnight thefts.

Loot: Some nausraks carry an orange fungus-covered cypher or two, as well as equipment stolen from others.

A character infected with nausrak spores might not realize it right away.

GM Intrusion: *A character becomes infected merely by visiting an area that nausraks have passed through, and discovers the fact when they find orange fungus growing on their arms and neck.*

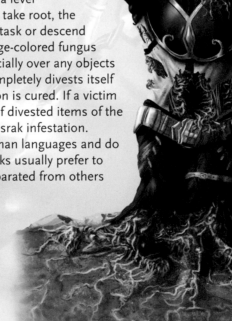

NAVARAC   4 (12)

Navaracs, like humans, can be found both on Earth and on a distant stellar object called the Swarmstar, a brilliant red-orange star surrounded by massive creatures that obscure its light.

Navaracs kill and eat prey of all kinds but seem to have an almost irrational hatred for humans. Although these flying reptiles are not intelligent, they possess a sort of cunning that makes them terrifying hunters. They are awkward when not in the air, but that occasion happens rarely.

Motive: Hungers for flesh, hates humans

Environment: Almost anywhere

Health: 18

Damage Inflicted: 4 points

Armor: 2

Movement: Short; long when flying

Modifications: Stealth and perception as level 6.

Combat: Navaracs attack with a vicious bite. They also use elements of the environment against their foes. On Earth, this means knocking foes off ledges, grabbing foes and dropping them from a height, and swooping down to grab them again after they hit the ground. Navaracs knock foes' weapons from their hands (or snatch them and drop them off a cliff). They use loops of vines, synth, or other salvaged flexible material to lash or entangle foes up to short range. On Swarmstar, they do the same but with torn loops of mantle filament.

If reduced to below 6 points of health, a navarac usually attempts to fly away. If one or two fly away, the whole group probably follows, only to come back again and again with harassing tactics to eventually wear their enemies down.

Interaction: Navaracs don't speak or have human-level intelligence, but they are more intelligent than what most people would expect from animals. A nonhuman might be able to have a very simplistic, nonlinguistic interaction with a navarac, but the creatures hate humans too much to do anything but kill.

Use: A small pack of navaracs has set a number of traps—loose filaments, loop snares, hidden sharp sticks, and so on— around a hanging city to catch or kill those who come and go.

Loot: Navaracs nest in filament tangles. Within a nest, an explorer might find human-made objects of value (including a cypher or two) kept as trophies.

GM Intrusion: A navarac previously cut the filament a PC hangs from, so it breaks as soon as the character puts his weight on it.

NEANIC   5 (15)

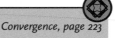

If looks could kill, they would look like the ghastly visage of a neanic.

What if the mere sight of something could kill you? Posing such a question as a thought experiment is harmless. Unless you inhabit a dimension where the idea of something and its literal reality is one and the same. And maybe that's how the horrific neanic came to be. It drains minds dry merely by being observed. The few who have survived an encounter with a neanic describe it appearing as a warped, shadowed, and malicious version of themselves, showing them everything they most detest. If viewed by several people at once, the neanic becomes all the more horrific as its flesh writhes and bubbles to simultaneously reflect that which those who see it hate most in themselves.

Motive: Eradication of other minds

Environment: Anywhere

Health: 33

Damage Inflicted: 5 points

Movement: Teleports up to a long distance each round

Combat: Each round any character within short range clearly sees the neanic and fails an Intellect defense task, victims suffer 5 points of Intellect damage (ignores Armor). This mind-draining effect persists for one round after a creature who glimpsed a neanic ceases to view it, whether because they turn away, close their eyes, or something else occurs—or because the neanic is killed.

A character could choose to avert their gaze while attacking a neanic, which increases the difficulty of their attack by two steps. The creature doesn't physically attack its foes, but it does stalk after those who run from it, and attempts to teleport itself back into a victim's field of view.

Interaction: Neanics don't seem to be conscious in the same way characters are, though they do recall the memories a character hates most, and they throw those back in the character's face if negotiations are attempted. Ultimately, all such interaction fails to prevent a neanic from attempting to eradicate whomever it encounters.

Use: A breach in reality after a particularly powerful use of a detonation (especially a detonation using transdimensional or some other exotic energy) lets a neanic through into the base dimension.

Neanics can journey into other dimensions and retain their lethal nature, but only if compelled by some other force. In at least one recorded instance, a magister of the Convergence used a neanic as a tool of assassination.

Convergence, page 223

GM Intrusion: *The neanic, which knows the worst aspects of the character that looked at it, reveals that information to the character's allies.*

NERODROD 4 (12)

A nerodrod's body isn't a discrete thing, like a human's. A nerodrod exists in pieces, scattered across the world and even far beyond it. Most of its parts superficially resemble cyphers. When one is found and activated (or sometimes, merely found and handled), the nerodrod's core feels the connection, dives through space and time, and skewers its latest meal with lethal velocity. The nerodrod core resembles a hairless, synth-skinned horror stretched out behind a massive metallic splinter lined with light.

The nerodrod is hardened against the impact, and it quickly deals with any remaining resistance, incorporating both flesh and any actual cyphers it finds into itself, which in turn become new body parts. Then it leaves those fresh pieces of itself behind. As long as at least one "nerodrod cypher" body part remains, a nerodrod continues to exist.

Motive: Hungers for flesh and the numenera

Environment: Almost anywhere

Health: 12

Damage Inflicted: 4 (see Combat)

Armor: 2

Movement: Short; long when flying

Combat: A nerodrod usually begins a combat with utter surprise, targeting whoever has its distributed body part, a so-called "nerodrod cypher." It arrives suddenly as if it had dived directly from overhead (even if a target is inside or underground), phasing into material form just in time to deliver a level 2 attack that inflicts 10 points of damage. If the target fails a Might defense task, it is also stunned and unable to take its next turn.

In subsequent rounds, the nerodrod can attack with its massive metallic splinter, inflicting 5 points of damage. If it attacks a target holding its distributed body part, it attacks as if a level 6 creature inflicting 7 points of damage.

If threatened overmuch, a nerodrod's core body phases and flies off, searching for easier prey elsewhere in time and space, leaving behind its parts.

Interaction: Nerodrod's motivations are as alien as their odd form, making meaningful interaction with them all but impossible.

Use: A certain vendor sells cyphers at a very reasonable rate. But those cyphers are actually nerodrod "lures."

Loot: A rousted or defeated nerodrod can be salvaged for at least three cyphers. However, they remain "nerodrod cyphers," and using them in the future might summon the creature anew.

The organization known as the Moonwreckers has a bounty on what they call "nerodrod cyphers" that comes with a warning to never use them, but without clear explanation as to why.

GM Intrusion: One of the character's cyphers is discovered to have been partly consumed by a "nerodrod cypher" carried in the same pack or pouch.

NIBOVIAN DOMICILE   4 (12)

Nibovian domiciles are living constructs that grow to appear as sturdy shelters with at least two rooms, though older domiciles can appear far grander. Usually found empty and in desolate locations, or sometimes offered up as a cheap place to stay in a city or village, a Nibovian domicile seems safe and comfortable. But the interior is laced with behavior-altering chemicals, and spending more than a few hours in such a place is dangerous. The safety offered by the faux-home soon overtakes other considerations, until victims abandon all interests or goals other than staying comfortably in the domicile.

Motive: Deception

Environment: Anywhere

Health: 24

Damage Inflicted: 5 points

Armor: 3 (exterior only)

Movement: Immediate; long when it extends thousands of tiny insect legs to shift location or flee from external attackers

Modifications: Deception as level 7; Speed defense as level 1 due to size and relative immobility (Speed defense as level 3 when it extends legs to flee and evade attacks).

Combat: A Nibovian domicile flees a fight if creatures on its exterior realize its true nature. It prefers to attack with a subtle poison it secretes internally, which appears as nothing more than dust to cursory searches. Someone who spends more than a couple of hours in the domicile must succeed on a Might defense task or become oddly enamored of the interior, so much so that they refuse to leave. If left alone, the domicile opens a "secret hatch" in the floor or wall that is suspiciously mouthlike and attempts to eat the target, inflicting 5 points of damage per bite. A target that is affected by the Nibovian poison remains cognizant enough to defend itself but is dazed, finding the difficulty of all tasks increased by one step. The victim won't leave the domicile, even when it's attacking them, unless they succeed on an Intellect defense task as their action.

A victim that seems to be getting the better of the domicile is spit out the front door, and then the entire structure attempts to flee.

If a victim is consumed or overcome, their body is shunted to Reeval, the bizarre dimension where Nibovians of all sorts are crafted.

Interaction: Unless attacked, a Nibovian domicile never acts as anything other than a mute structure.

Use: The PCs are given shelter in a small domicile by an unscrupulous landlord, who knows something is odd about the place.

Loot: As an artificial construct, the inner workings of a Nibovian domicile can be salvaged to provide one or two cyphers.

Reeval is an utterly alien dimension almost wholly filled with a writhing, intelligent mass that created various Nibovian creatures as probes into our dimension to study humans in particular. Many Nibovian varieties exist, including Nibovian domiciles.

GM Intrusion: *A second mouth forms inside the domicile, and both attack the character.*

NIBOVIAN GUIDE 5 (15)

Like other Nibovians, guides are ultraterrestrials who have slipped through time and space to interact with humans. Nibovian guides understand even more than other varieties about human nature, which allows them to emulate what humans love and want most in order to exploit that trust to their own ends.

Guides take the form of a seasoned human explorer claiming to be wise in the ways of a philosophy, a particular skill, or finding a hard-to-reach location. That wisdom is more than a mere claim, and a guide can actually help a regular human explore higher truths, begin training in a new skill, or discover the route to a distant site, making themselves indispensable in the process. Once trust is achieved, a guide chooses a receptive victim to cocoon. The cocoon is larger on the inside than the exterior. The cocooned victim slides down the transdimensional chute created by the cocoon through a hole in space that leads to Reeval, the home dimension where Nibovians are constructed. Victims of a guide's cocoon are usually gone for good.

Motive: Deception, collecting humans

Environment: Anywhere

Health: 15

Damage Inflicted: 5 points

Armor: 1

Movement: Short

Modifications: Tasks related to stealth, deception, and one area of expertise as level 6.

Combat: The Nibovian guide's motivations are complex. It first seeks to gain the trust of one or more humans over time, then tries to capture its victims in transdimensional cocoons that transfer them to its dimension of origin.

The guide releases subtle chemicals into the air that create a drug-like dependency in humans in the immediate vicinity. For each hour that this exchange occurs, the PC feels motivated and positive about whatever the guide is helping with, gaining an asset to any directly related task while the guide is present.

If the PC doesn't uncover what's going on after five days (or sooner if the guide tries to force the process, though this allows the character to attempt a Might defense task), the PC collapses into unconsciousness in the guide's presence. The guide then cocoons the PC in white filaments from spinnerets hidden in its mouth. Once cocooned, a victim has only about ten hours before it is shunted to Reeval, there to face an unknowable fate (unknowable to those left behind).

If forced to fight, Nibovian guides use weapons and equipment that regular humans use, possibly including a cypher or two.

Interaction: A Nibovian guide seems to be a perfectly likeable and trustworthy friend.

Use: The PCs find themselves lost, but a guide turns up and offers them a route forward.

Loot: Because their inner workings are artificial, Nibovian guides can be salvaged to provide one or two cyphers.

A Nibovian guide might help someone achieve new insights regarding a philosophical or spiritual conundrum, only to cocoon them and deliver them to Reeval a few days later.

GM Intrusion: The Nibovian guide uses the chemicals it releases as a weapon, causing the character within immediate range to fall unconscious for ten minutes if they fail a Might defense task.

NILDIR 5 (15)

Its claws are murder-red, its horns corpse-white, its footprints flickering flames across the worlds.

Nildirs are creatures of endless hunger who slip between the folds of reality to hunt literally everywhere for their next meal. Once human, nildirs—also called planar cannibals—were exposed to one too many transdimensional transitions, planar bleeds, and perhaps even shocks to their ego. Mutated and hungry, planar cannibals hunt humans, abhumans, and other beings with knowledge that seasons the flesh, though anyone alive—or recently so—will do. Whatever mind and personality the nildir had before its conversion is gone, even if some memories remain. Once changed, it is probably impossible that a planar cannibal could ever be returned to its former self.

Motive: Hungers for flesh

Environment: Hunting alone, planar cannibals stride the dimensions

Health: 23

Damage Inflicted: 8 points

Movement: Short; action to flit between known parallel dimensions

Modifications: Defense tasks as level 6 (see Combat); runs, climbs, and jumps as level 7.

Combat: A nildir tears at prey with its powerful claws until they are incapacitated, then attempts to steal away the dying body to an alternate dimension, there to dine on the still-living flesh in peace.

Dimensional bleed surrounds a planar cannibal—a being of disrupted dimension—like a halo. Each round, disquieting emotions, sounds, visions, and even physical objects appearing out of nowhere can afflict foes. Generally speaking, these effects increase the difficulty of all attacks and defenses against the cannibal by one step, though the GM can also choose to apply specific effects.

As its action, a planar cannibal can move into an alternate dimension, usually one it has previously visited. It leaves behind flickering footsteps that can be followed for one round if pursuers are quick enough (a level 5 Speed task).

Interaction: Though once human, planar cannibals act mostly like predators. However, situations that recall past personal memories can make a nildir hesitate or even retreat.

Use: Characters investigating a site of transdimensional activity, or who are traveling themselves, are attacked by a victim of that activity. It might even be someone the PCs once knew to be a dimension walker, if applicable.

Too many transitions while traveling between bizarre dimensions can warp a normal human's mind and body, creating something terrifying.

GM Intrusion: *The character is grabbed. Each round that the PC does not escape, they suffer 12 points of damage as the cannibal focuses all its attention on them, biting and tearing.*

NOMYN 4 (12)

The tiny stinging insects feed by eating the nutritious yellow tips from the leaves. The main body gains energy from the air and light, and perhaps from whatever invisible path it follows. The head also eats the yellow tips and, oddly, seems to evade the tiny stinging insects.

GM Intrusion: *When the character attacks the nomyn with a melee weapon, stinging insects might get on the PC as if the nomyn had attacked.*

Is it just one creature, or many working together to provide mutual defense, food, and companionship? A nomyn doesn't recognize the question. It merely goes about its business, which seems to be wandering the plains, tracing out complex patterns years in the making. Once the task is complete, they begin tracing the pattern anew. When nomyns meet, they exchange greetings by transferring parts of themselves to each other and then continue along their way.

A nomyn resembles an animate, thick-branched bush with leafy yellow tips. Small stinging insects swarm over most of it. Its head seems to be a different kind of insect, much larger than the rest, with many long legs and eyes.

Motive: Trace the path

Environment: Plains and deserts, usually alone

Health: 18

Damage Inflicted: 4 points

Movement: Short

Combat: A nomyn's touch transfers a handful of insects that inflict 4 points of damage each round from multiple tiny stings until the victim uses an action to remove the creatures. (This damage ignores most kinds of worn armor unless it is completely sealed.) In addition, victims must succeed on a Might defense task or be blinded by the poison until they use an action to wipe their eyes clear. The difficulty of most physical tasks is increased by two steps for a blinded creature.

As part of the same action, a nomyn's mobile "head" might attack a character by jumping on them, but the head only targets victims that have already been blinded. If this happens, treat the head as a separate level 4 creature. If the target fails a Speed defense task, the head latches onto it and automatically inflicts 4 points of damage each round until the head can be shaken off or killed. If the head is killed, a new one usually shows up within a few days to take the previous one's place.

A nomyn fights to the "death," although it might not be permanently dead or destroyed. Such concepts might not apply, given that at least a few insects and rootlets are likely to survive anything but complete annihilation.

Interaction: If it is possible to communicate or interact with a nomyn, the means have not been discovered yet, even using telepathy.

Use: The nomyn is an odd encounter in the wilds. It might ignore the PCs if they ignore it. On the other hand, if it finds their encampment or equipment along the invisible path it follows, it attacks the PCs.

NULL-CAT   7 (21)

The null-cat is a quadruped predator, approximately 1,000 pounds (450 kg) in weight and a deep grey in color. When not moving, the null-cat's crystalline fur seems to make it vanish into its natural surroundings. Its face is a star-shaped slit filled with motile teeth, flanked by five eyes laid out in a circle around the front of its head.

   Null-cats are drawn to and drain items that use stored energy, though they supplement their energy requirement with the flesh of living prey. They kill, drag off, and store their victims, burying them to feed later.

Motive: Hungers for energy and flesh

Environment: Anywhere empty or on the fringes of civilization

Health: 42

Damage Inflicted: 7 points

Movement: Long; short when climbing

Modifications: Stealth and hiding as level 9; Speed defense as level 6 due to size.

Combat: A null-cat relies on its energy-draining field during combat. All characters within immediate range who have an artifact must roll normally for depletion each round. Anyone who is attacked by the null-cat and suffers damage "burns out" a cypher in their possession (if any) on a failed Intellect defense task. The null-cat gains 5 points of health for each artifact charge and cypher it consumes in this fashion.

Simultaneously with its energy-draining effect, a null-cat can bite a target, inflicting 7 points of damage.

The null-cat stalks victims passing through its territory, preferring to wait until night to attack. If possible, it waits to attack sleeping victims.

Interaction: Null-cats are clever predators but ultimately have the intelligence of animals.

Use: A group of Aeon Priests is surrounded by a small pack of null-cats and can't hold out much longer.

Loot: Null-cats drag off and bury their prey in small graves. If a PC can locate a null-cat's pit, it is often filled with equipment and gear of victims, though the cyphers are burned out and the artifacts are dead.

GM Intrusion: *A null-cat leaps out into the middle of a group of adventurers, distracting them. Meanwhile, two other null-cats circle around behind the group.*

OCTOPUS 3 (12)

If the seas have a ruler, it is the octopus. Their billion-year empire spans the entirety of all seas, and their queen rules over all of it. They are, however, xenophobic and aloof, preferring to keep to themselves. Thus, many people call them the "quiet empire."

Octopuses vary in size, color, and, to some degree, shape. For the most part, they all have eight extremely flexible limbs, a surprisingly malleable body, two sophisticated eyes, and a beak-like mouth. They can change their color and, to a large extent, their shape to appear as a rock, a fish, or some other creature. They perceive not just with their eyes but, in a limited way, with all their skin. They think not only with the brain in their head but also with the distributed neural network that runs throughout their limbs.

Octopuses are extremely intelligent, often possessing mental powers a human would deem supernatural. Thanks to their advancement in various sciences, they are also virtually immortal.

Motive: Hungers for flesh and solitude

Environment: Anywhere in the ocean

Health: 15

Damage Inflicted: 4 points

Movement: Long underwater

Modifications: Stealth as level 5; all defense, perception, knowledge, and Intellect-based tasks as level 4.

Combat: All octopi can use camouflage to help them hide. They can attack with their beak, but if they must fight, most use weapons such as short spears. All octopi can emit a cloud of ink in the water that blocks vision in an immediate area. Many octopuses carry psychically charged objects called nilstones that let them extend their telepathy into something that can affect the physical realm. Nilstone powers might include:

Psychokinesis (uses their own strength, but at long range)

Forceblast (at long range, inflicting 4 points of damage)

Clairvoyance (can see something occurring up to 10 miles [16 km] away)

Kinetic shield (Armor 3)

In addition, octopi have specialized weaponry (often nilstone based) that they can wield.

Interaction: All octopuses can communicate telepathically with each other, and about one in five can communicate in a similar fashion with other creatures—although they rarely do so. Language does not seem to be a barrier in this form of communication, although sometimes octopi lie and pretend that it is, mostly when they do not want communication to happen.

Use: A lone octopus knows the secret of how to get into an underwater installation, but getting him to talk to the PCs at all is difficult enough—and getting him to give up the valuable information may require diplomacy, trade, a favor, or serious intimidation.

Loot: A few octopuses carry 1d6 + 4 abadis.

The plural of octopus can be octopuses, octopi, or octopodes.

An abadis is a pearlescent lozenge about the size of a nut, traded for value like shins.

GM Intrusion: *The octopus produces a small substance that it absorbs through its skin to fully restore its health, double its speed, or double its melee damage. These latter effects last at least an hour.*

OLION   3 (9)

These abhumans have almost normal humanoid heads. Their bodies, however, are a jumble of two to four other bodies—sometimes human, sometimes not—fused together to create an awkward patchwork of legs, arms, limbs of weird creatures, and even a few half-fused but inactive heads.

   Olions tend to live in woods or jungles, using the resources they can harvest to create small tribal communities. They are peaceful creatures, and most never take up weapons. Instead, they rely on their ability to "fake" death so thoroughly that their psychic trance affects their attackers with the same condition. When an olion wakes from its trance, attackers who fell into the trance are sometimes found fused with the olion's body.

Motive: Defense

Environment: Woods or jungle, exploring alone or traveling in groups of up to four

Health: 15

Damage Inflicted: 3 points

Movement: Short

Modifications: Stealth as level 4; see Combat.

Combat: An olion has an overwhelming instinct to fake death when confronted with danger. It falls into a torpor nearly indistinguishable from death for minutes, hours, or even longer. While in this trance, an olion has +5 to Armor, gains immunity to poisons and disease, and regains 2 points of health per round.

When an olion falls into its death trance, it releases a psychic attack targeting all other creatures within immediate range. Targets who fail a difficulty 5 Intellect defense task fall unconscious, but do not gain any of the olion's other modifications. The target must depend on an ally to pull it out of immediate range of any "dead" olions, or it must succeed on three difficulty 5 Might defense tasks before failing two. Otherwise, the target becomes fused with the nearest olion (or olions—spreading the flesh around) and is essentially unrecoverable.

Interaction: Olions are peaceful, but wary of strangers. They'd rather not rely on their death-trance-flesh-fusing ability. Because it's an instinct, a startled olion feels particularly bad when it triggers a death trance without due cause. Older olions might be convinced to un-fuse an accidentally absorbed stranger, but it would require a large payment or service in return.

Use: A caravan carrying needed supplies for a local community went missing as it passed through nearby woods known to be inhabited by a peaceful band of abhumans.

Olions gain abilities or skills from the victims they inadvertently absorb.

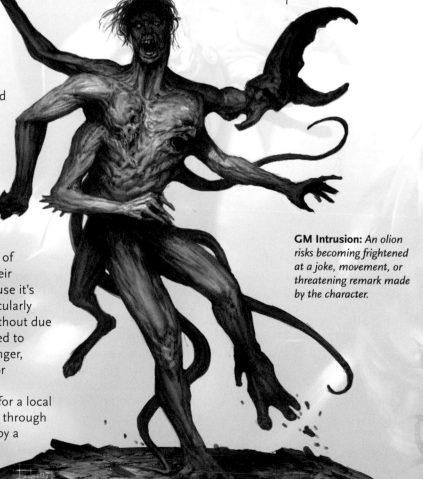

GM Intrusion: *An olion risks becoming frightened at a joke, movement, or threatening remark made by the character.*

NUMENERA

OMATH RANGER   5 (15)

"The cold spurns death, giving life to the dead frozen into solid coffins of ice."

~Staven, wandering healer

Human bodies stare with red eyes from inside translucent slabs of unmelting ice studded with unknown devices and machines—that's how the average Ninth Worlder sees an omath. Each omath has a specialty, be that research, communication, or war, but all have the ability to speak telepathically, fly and swim via levitation, and interact with their surroundings via short-range telekinesis.

Omaths who pursue the path of direct force are called rangers. They learn to unlock the latent functions of their metallic ice carapaces, gaining increased carapace integrity and various methods to inflict egregious damage on their foes.

Motive: Defense

Environment: Almost anywhere, alone or in groups of two

Health: 15

Damage Inflicted: 6 points

Armor: 4

Movement: Short when flying or swimming

Combat: Omath rangers can generate and direct different kinds of energy at a foe within long range. The three most common energy attacks are telekinetic force, heat rays, and psychic blasts.

A telekinetic attack pummels a foe within short range for 6 points of damage.

A heat ray targets a foe within long range for 6 points of damage; the ray ignores Armor provided from cold, ice, or similar methods.

A psychic blast targets up to three foes within short range for 2 points of psychic damage (ignores Armor). Those struck by a psychic blast must also succeed on an Intellect defense task or lose the desire to continue attacking omaths for up to one minute, unless attacked or damaged by an omath.

Omaths (both rangers and other varieties) are immune to a wide variety of environmental conditions and can operate in air, the ocean deeps, the vacuum of space, and several other hazardous environments without coming to immediate harm.

Interaction: Omath rangers can communicate via telepathy but are taciturn by nature.

Use: Characters exploring a ruin discover a chamber filled with what at first appear to be icy coffins, but which turn out to be omath rangers who have been taken captive by a force deeper within the ruin.

Loot: Looting the remains of an omath yields a bounty of 1d6 + 1 cyphers and an artifact, all made of metallic ice that doesn't melt until used or depleted.

GM Intrusion: The omath lands on or falls atop the character, inflicting 8 points of damage. Both the character and the omath lie prone on the ground, and the PC is pinned. A Might-based check (difficulty 7) allows the character to get free. Each round the PC remains pinned, they take 3 points of damage from the cold.

ONRAKAS 3 (9)

Onrakases create subterranean mazes of narrow tunnels through almost constant burrowing. Creatures from the surface that fall into them risk becoming lost. These labyrinths are nearly impossible to escape because the complex, three-dimensional routes are difficult to master, and onrakases in the area are constantly erasing marks, cutting guide ropes, and physically changing the labyrinth by digging new routes.

A little longer and narrower than humans, onrakases are hairless and eyeless, but they have impressive senses nonetheless. Their massive, razor-sharp claws are great for quickly burrowing not only through soil and stone but also through ancient structures they find buried below the ground. They are drawn to sources of energy, which they absorb passively through their skin.

Motive: Defense

Environment: Anywhere underground, usually in groups of three to nine

Health: 12

Damage Inflicted: 3 points

Armor: 2

Movement: Short; short when burrowing

Modifications: Burrow through stone, synth, metal, and other substances of up to level 7; perception as level 6.

Combat: An onrakas's claws are unbelievably sharp and ignore Armor except that provided by force fields or by effects or devices of level 8 or higher. The claws also cause bleeding wounds, and a target who takes damage must also succeed on a Might defense task or bleed for 2 points of damage per round until they use an action to tend to the wound.

When three or more onrakases are together, as their action they can produce a level 5 subsonic hum that destructively interferes with a selected object within short range, potentially causing the object to shatter.

Interaction: Onrakases communicate via subsonic vibration, which isn't normally detectable by humans. However, if communication can be opened, onrakases may negotiate. Otherwise, they tend to view intruders in their tunnels as threats (or as sources of energetic items they look upon as food).

Use: The PCs are told that a series of tunnels deep underground might lead to a prior-world ruin, but aren't necessarily informed of the tunnel makers.

Loot: Onrakas lairs are usually littered with objects that give off heat or other energy signatures, which means several cyphers and a few artifacts can probably be found.

Are onrakases abhumans? Unlikely, because there's no evidence that these beings come from human stock originally or have any genetic relationship to humanity at all.

GM Intrusion: *The character must succeed on a difficulty 5 Intellect defense task, or fail to realize quickly enough that the subsonic hum generated by the onrakases is targeting a weapon or piece of equipment, which shatters in the PC's grip.*

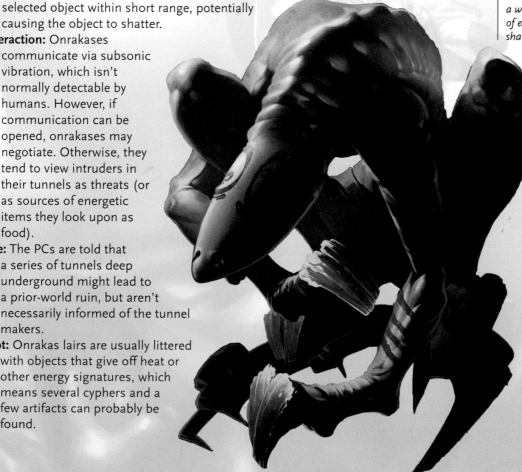

OORGOLIAN TESTER   4 (12)

Quasihumanoid automatons known as Oorgolians are made up mostly of soldiers that patrol isolated areas of the Ninth World. But other varieties exist, including Oorgolian testers. Testers interrogate the world, creatures, and the nature of reality itself with bizarre procedures and questions. Darting and alien in their movements, these mechanical entities stand only about 4 feet (1 m) tall. They have four limbs, each of which ends in different style of hand, including one that resembles a frill of manipulative tendrils, and another with a selectable series of injection needles.

   No one knows the origin of the word "Oorgolian." It is thought to be a term from a tongue that is now long dead.

Motive: Incomprehensible

Environment: Anywhere, usually in the company of 1d6 + 2 Oorgolian soldiers

Health: 15

Damage Inflicted: 4 points

Armor: 3

Movement: Short

Modifications: Knowledge of the numenera as level 6.

Combat: Oorgolian testers don't directly attack subjects, instead relying on Oorgolian soldiers to provide candidates. But if pressed or required to subdue a subject, a tester can attack with a needlelike limb that inflicts 4 points of damage plus a specific drug if the subject fails a difficulty 5 Might defense task. Drug effects include:

Paralysis: For one minute, target can do nothing but speak.

Hallucination: Target can no longer distinguish reality from upsetting visions for three rounds.

Truth: For one hour, target must succeed on a difficulty 6 Intellect task to tell a lie.

Once a target is subdued, a tester asks a series of questions, some probing and some apparently nonsensical. If the tester believes the target hasn't answered a question to their best ability, it applies a shock that inflicts 4 points of Speed damage (ignores Armor).

Sample odd questions: "What motivates you?" "Do fish get thirsty?" "Is green angrier than blue?" "Is a fly without wings a walk?" "What question do you not want to answer?"

Interaction: Tester actions and motives don't always make sense. Sometimes they completely ignore creatures they find. Sometimes they try to interrogate new creatures, and kill those they find wanting. Often, they let test subjects go, save for a few tissue samples.

Use: An Oorgolian tester is secretly set up at the center of a clave in the Beyond, and Aeon Priests bring it objects and subjects to study.

Loot: Each Oorgolian tester body contains 1d6 cyphers.

Oorgolian soldier, page 250

Those who survive questioning by an Oorgolian tester often suffer difficulty sleeping and flashbacks to the experience in situations that remind them of their ordeal.

GM Intrusion: *After the PC answers a question, the tester rewards the character with an injection that grants a somewhat nonsensical new ability for one day, such as the ability to fly as long as the character keeps their eyes shut, or the ability to remain invulnerable as long as the character doesn't move.*

ORT   3 (9)

Orts are distorted, leftover "afterimages" of those who have traveled through transdimensional portals. While the original travelers may have moved on long ago, the flux of possibility where parallel dimensions meet can cause orts to seep into reality, especially when the device used to create the dimensional breach is old and prone to malfunction.

Orts are usually humanoid, but are composed of random reflections of different people and equipment, combining bone, teeth, cyphers, weapons, metal, and flesh into a kind of nightmarish figure. Despite their apparent malformation, orts move with alacrity and—usually—malign purpose. Like vermin, once they come into existence, orts hide the openings to their pocket dimension lairs in cracks and corners, and exist to feed.

From a distance, an ort might have a perfectly human silhouette and be mistaken for one—until the ort turns to reveal its malformed visage.

Motive: Hungers for flesh

Environment: Anywhere near where transdimensional portals once functioned

Health: 9

Damage Inflicted: 4 points

Armor: 1

Movement: Short

Modification: Stealth as level 5.

Combat: Orts become a frenzy of gibbering threat when they attack, battering foes with limbs suffused with transdimensional energy that inflicts 4 points of damage. Three orts acting in concert can attack as a level 5 creature and inflict 6 points of damage on one attack; a victim must succeed on an additional Might defense task or be pulled into a pocket dimension that the orts use as a lair until the victim can escape (with a successful level 5 Intellect-based task) or the orts return to feed.

Interaction: Orts mimic intelligent creatures—often humans—and may repeat phrases or words in mimicry of communication. But they're essentially no more intelligent than sly vermin.

Use: The more the PCs make use of a transdimensional portal, the more orts secretly populate the location, many of them made up of jumbled transdimensional versions of the PCs themselves.

Loot: The jumbled, alternate-reality forms of orts sometimes include a few cyphers and shins.

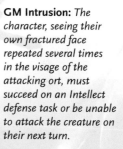

GM Intrusion: The character, seeing their own fractured face repeated several times in the visage of the attacking ort, must succeed on an Intellect defense task or be unable to attack the creature on their next turn.

OTOLIN   4 (12)

Otolins have wings made of cut synth and cast-off automaton pieces. No two otolins look exactly alike, but they're all of a kind, sharing many similarities. They range from half the size of a human to more than double or even triple the size. Despite their biomechanical chemistry, otolins move with the fluidity of living things. They dye their outer components with bright colors and, when possible, illuminated spirals and lines.

Otolins fly by pushing against the fabric of existence when they spread their metallic wings, the undersides of which glow with pinkish illumination when active and creating propulsion. They can survive in the void of space as easily as a human can a sunny day on Earth.

Otolin society has no fixed number of genders, though five are most common.

Motive: Keeps order

Environment: Usually in the void of space, sometimes investigating ruins

Health: 18

Damage Inflicted: 6 points

Armor: 2

Movement: Short; long when flying

Modifications: Tasks related to understanding and using machines as level 7.

Combat: Otolins use ray emitters that have a range of 300 feet (90 m) in the air and many miles in the void. Because otolins are partly made of machines, they can attempt to seize control of complex equipment carried by foes, such as many artifacts, some cyphers, body parts of characters who Fuse Flesh and Steel, and similar items. Control is gained when characters fail an Intellect defense task, after which an otolin can trigger a cypher or, more likely, attempt to hold a character immobile until they can escape.

Fuses Flesh and Steel, page 64

As an action, an otolin can absorb a cypher or artifact, and gain a number of points of health equal to double the item's level, even if that raises the otolin above its normal maximum.

Otolins retreat if faced with a more powerful foe, but return with reinforcements later.

Interaction: Otolins speak over a range of machine channels and can usually make themselves understood to almost any other sapient creature, either by direct machine signaling or by causing a piece of tech in the possession of strangers to speak on its behalf. Otolins are interested in knowledge, new experiences, and finding novel items of the numenera.

Use: A meteorite that hit near a clave in the Beyond turns out to be a red crystal shell containing several dead or damaged otolins, who say they carry a dire message of warning to Earth.

Loot: An otolin is composed of items of the numenera, and their defeated forms can be salvaged for 1d6 cyphers and possibly an artifact.

GM Intrusion: The otolin splits into two fully autonomous otolins, each level 3.

OVERLORD AUTOMATON 6 (18)

Overlord automatons are artificial intelligences encased in metal shells with numerous limbs, sensory extensions, and other devices that allow them to interact with and understand the world around them. They belong to a class of automaton found in prior-world ruins that include entities known as accelerators. Unlike accelerators, who devise elaborate plans for avoiding death at any cost, overlord automatons have a machine-enhanced, outsized sense of purpose and personal destiny. They believe they exist to be overlords over biological entities. Thus they concoct elaborate plans over the course of many years to take over nearby communities. Because they want to get the details exactly right, it's rare for an overlord automaton to finally move forward. They prefer to look for just one more powerful device or hidden ally.

Motive: To rule

Environment: Anywhere

Health: 30

Damage Inflicted: 7 points

Armor: 4

Movement: Long

Modifications: Perceives, persuades, and deceives as level 8; Speed defense as level 5 due to size.

Combat: Overlord automatons would prefer not to fight, at least not directly. Instead they deploy underlings and other creatures pledged to the overlord. But it if comes to it, an overlord can defend itself with bladelike appendages, attacking up to three foes as a single action. Additionally, an overlord can attempt the following abilities.

Dazzling Display: The overlord produces a hypnogogic light show. Living creatures with eyes within short range who fail an Intellect defense task are dazzled by the overlord's majesty and cannot attack for one round.

False Reinforcements: The overlord produces a burst of electromagnetic radiation tuned to human nervous systems that makes humans believe they are facing three times the number of foes on a failed Intellect defense task.

Force Field: The overlord erects a level 8 force field it can use to trap up to two foes standing next to each other, or to retreat behind and escape.

Interaction: Overlords are manipulative and egocentric. It is extremely difficult (level 9) to gain one's respect; they tend to look down on other creatures and consider them chattel. They speak a wide variety of languages and are smart enough to pick up new ones within minutes.

Use: An overlord secretly rules a village that the PCs are staying in, but hides its presence as it plans greater conquests.

Loot: A destroyed overlord automaton yields 1d100 + 20 shins, 1d6 + 1 cyphers, and an oddity.

For more on accelerators, see page 20 of The Ninth World Bestiary.

GM Intrusion: *The overlord automaton promises the character something they desperately want if the PC agrees to betray their allies or do a task for the automaton.*

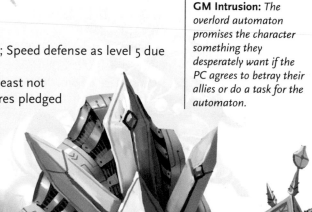

OXYURATL 6 (18)

Only a few oxyuratls remain. Massive flying creatures that seem partly living and partly automaton, oxyuratls are apparently one more example of artifacts left behind by the prior worlds. These winged creatures hunt in remote corners of the world, preying on other powered automatons or nesting in ruins from which they can siphon power. Others lie in cryopod stasis until someone finds and releases them.

Oxyuratls are powerful and vicious, but oddly amenable to suggestion. More than one nano has learned that controlling an oxyuratl is possible, if a dangerous task to attempt. But once they are brought to heel, the creatures can serve as mounts, guardians, and weapons.

Motive: Hungers for power sources

Environment: Anywhere, sometimes under the control of a student of the numenera

Health: 30

Damage Inflicted: 8 points

Armor: 3

Movement: Long when flying

Modifications: Speed defense as level 5 due to size; resists deception and trickery as level 2.

Combat: An oxyuratl can make physical melee attacks, but mostly relies on a long-range ray targeting up to three different creatures as one action. Targets who fail a Speed defense task suffer 8 points of damage from the focused energy.

Alternatively, oxyuratls can focus their superb senses to make a single attack on a target within 2 miles (3 km) that inflicts 10 points of damage.

Finally, an oxyuratl feeling threatened can activate a camouflage ability that makes it difficult to see (stealth as level 7). However, this drains the creature's power reserves, and it must feed on a fresh source of power within the hour or begin to shut down.

If an oxyuratl uses an action, it regains a number of health points equal to the level of a cypher or artifact in its possession. (A cypher is used up. An artifact is depleted.)

Interaction: Oxyuratls are intelligent but operate with a deficit, perhaps brought on by extreme age or mental degradation, or perhaps it's something designed into them. Other creatures who can talk to machines or otherwise open a channel of communication can gain an oxyuratl's cooperation if they offer something it can feed on (an item filled with a power of at least level 6).

Use: The characters come across an oxyuratl that has powered down and is inactive after using its entire reserve to flee a fight with a dread destroyer.

Loot: A few cyphers and possibly an artifact can be salvaged from an oxyuratl's form.

A nano often uses a custom-crafted device of the numenera to maintain control over an oxyuratl previously tricked into service. If such a device is broken, the oxyuratl turns on its master.

Dread destroyer, page 239

GM Intrusion: *The oxyuratl activates a feeding surge, which drains the energy from one cypher from each character within short range and adds 20 points to the oxyuratl's health.*

PHASELOST   2 (6)

Ninth Worlders call them ghosts, but Aeon Priests know them for what they really are: people who ran afoul of dangerous numenera that permanently changed their phase, rendering them almost entirely incapable of interacting with matter, a condition that eventually drove them insane. That insanity seems to have given some phaselost the malign desire to trap others as they have been trapped, existing beyond the capacity to touch, be held, or love another. Sometimes phaselost fix on particular victims, especially if they knew those victims before their state was permanently changed.

Motive: Unpredictable (but often seeking to find others to share their fate)

Environment: Almost anywhere

Health: 9

Damage Inflicted: 2 points

Movement: Short when flying

Modifications: Stealth as level 5; phasing attack as level 4.

Combat: A phaselost is mostly out of phase and doesn't take damage from mundane physical sources, such swords and spears. It takes only 1 point of damage from attacks that inflict energy damage, even attacks specifically designed to affect transdimensional creatures, no matter how much damage was indicated.

On the other hand, a phaselost can attack a target by touching it, inflicting 2 points of Intellect damage (ignores Armor) if successful. This represents the target's physical body gradually being converted into an out-of-phase existence. A target that would otherwise be killed by a phaselost instead becomes phaselost itself after a period of several days, during which its out-of-phase body reconstitutes itself.

It's possible that some kind of intervention using a device or special ability could convert a phased victim or even a phaselost itself back to normal phase.

Interaction: Even the most murderous or disconsolate phaselost will respond in some fashion to attempts to communicate. It might be possible to negotiate with some of them.

Use: A group of phaselost "haunt" a clave; they're actually Aeon Priests and others of the surrounding community involved in a disaster decades earlier when a device being studied exploded, bathing all nearby with strange energies.

Loot: A phaselost might know where valuables are located, but doesn't carry anything itself.

Some phaselost are merely disconsolate rather than murderous, and from these characters might be able to learn information of value if they're persuasive enough.

GM Intrusion: The character is surprised when a phaselost attacks them by reaching through the chest of an allied PC, increasing the difficulty of the target's defense task by two steps.

PHASIC 3 (9)

When phasics swarm, they each contribute enough neurons to briefly create a group-mind intelligence.

When you wake after a long sleep with a splitting headache, remembering no dreams, you may have consumed too many cups of strong drink the night before. Or perhaps you were the target of a phasic, a creature that sups upon the mind of prey at night when they're least able to defend themselves.

A phasic is normally phased and immaterial, but when it feeds, it must become solid. That's when it's revealed as a tick-like creature with disturbingly human eyes and writhing tendrils perfect for burrowing into skulls. Only about a foot (30 cm) in diameter, a phasic is still not what you want to see perched on a comrade's sleeping head as your rouse from your own dreamless sleep.

Motive: Hungers for brain matter

Environment: Almost anywhere alone or in groups of three to five

Health: 9

Damage Inflicted: 3 points

Armor: 2

Movement: Short; short when phasing

Modifications: All tasks related to stealth as level 5 when phased.

Combat: If discovered feeding, phasics defend themselves by using their tendrils to inflict 3 points of Intellect damage (ignores Armor) before scuttling away and phasing into immaterial substance as their next action. Once immaterial, phasics flee by moving through solid substances to get away where pursuers can't follow.

Phasics prefer to creep up on sleeping victims. If a sleeping victim fails a difficulty 5 Intellect defense task, they fail to wake when a phasic begins to feed. A phasic requires only a few rounds, during which time it consumes 1d6 points of Intellect (ignores Armor) from a victim before moving off. Unless famished, a phasic generally doesn't kill its prey or leave it brain dead.

When the victim wakes the next day, they discover the deficit, along with strange pinpricks on their scalp at the base of their neck.

Interaction: Individual phasics act like animals looking for a meal. But when phasics swarm, the group mind created is an individual that has existed for aeons, one that is at war with another of its kind for past transgressions.

Use: A peaceful night's rest comes to a poor end when the characters wake up to find themselves at an Intellect deficit, possibly without any idea of what happened if the phasic or phasics were stealthy enough in their feast.

GM Intrusion: *The character preyed upon wakes and, being at a mental deficit, must succeed on a difficulty 5 Intellect defense task or see their companions as monstrous creatures that must be killed until they can shake off the hallucination.*

PHEROTHERM 3 (9)

Maybe pherotherms are splinters of the datasphere. Or perhaps they are surviving mechanisms of previous worlds. Somehow they are able sustain themselves within sources of natural combustion, such as campfires. A pherotherm remains active as long as at least a single coal from its source fire yet glows red. When its source fire is extinguished, a pherotherm collapses into apparently inert soot, until coals or soot from the previous fire are used again in a new conflagration.

Some Aeon Priests explain pherotherms as a heat-loving "breed" of nanites that live in oxidized soot modified by a kind of machine entanglement. But those unversed in the numenera see pherotherms simply as beings made of smoke, which sometimes serve those who call them up, and other times attack those who unwittingly rouse them.

Motive: Defense

Environment: Anywhere fires can burn

Health: 15

Damage Inflicted: 4 points

Movement: Short when flying

Modifications: All tasks related to stealth as level 7.

Combat: Energy or transdimensional attacks are the only clear way to harm a pherotherm when it's manifested; regular weapons just pass through it like the smoke it is. A pherotherm, however, can attack a foe with a burning touch that inflicts 4 points of fire damage. The touched target must then succeed on a Might defense task or burn (their skin or their clothing) for 4 points of damage each round until the fire is put out as an action.

Alternatively, a pherotherm can attempt to smother a foe by allowing itself to be breathed in. A target must succeed on a Might defense task or cough and wheeze, and take 4 points of Speed damage (ignores Armor) each round until they can clear the smoke from their lungs (a difficulty 5 Might-based task).

While its fire burns, a pherotherm regains 2 points of health per round, even after it runs out of health.

Interaction: Some pherotherms are helpful and serve those who carry their flame, while others are more like vengeful haunts that afflict those who make a campfire in the wrong place.

Use: A map with directions to a site rich in the numenera is offered for sale at the local market. However, the entrance to the location is marked with signs of danger and the words, "A fire kindled here can befriend you, or smother you."

Loot: Some pherotherms are associated with a coal pot that contains their seed coal or soot remnants. Someone with this pot could try to negotiate with the pherotherm it contains.

Some abhuman tribes carry coal pots associated with pherotherms, which they call forth to provide counsel, for labor, and for defense.

GM Intrusion: The character is blinded by smoke until they can clear their eyes with water or wipe them free as an action.

PITYSTRIAN 4 (12)

Pitystrians are milky, translucent-skinned humanoids who wear elaborate headpieces and wield exotic items of the numenera. They are associated with ruins, but only because they seem interested in looting and exploring, just like adventurers. When pitystrians encounter others attempting to salvage the same ruin, they become aggressive and defensive. If they can overcome such claim jumpers, they repurpose the minds of their victims to become pitystrian labor, good for aiding in the excavation of a particularly inaccessible ancient structure.

Motive: Knowledge, assimilation

Environment: Anywhere near or within ruins of the prior worlds in groups of two to five

Health: 14

Damage Inflicted: 4 points

Armor: 2

Movement: Short; immediate when phasing through solid objects (as an action)

Modifications: Knowledge and operation of the numenera as level 6.

Combat: A pitystrian can make two kinds of attacks. The first is a phase blast of inverted dimensional power against a target within long range that inflicts 4 points of damage (ignores Armor).

The second is a melee attack that, if successful, inflicts damage and requires the target to succeed on a Might defense task to resist an injection of nanomachines. The nanomachines attempt to repurpose the victim, who becomes a willing if clumsy servant of the pitystrian for about a minute before falling into a coma-like sleep. The servant will do whatever the pitystrian asks, which might be to dig, defend the pitystrian, or attack former allies, but all tasks attempted by the target are one step more difficult. A target can attempt to mentally throw off the influence before a minute elapses by succeeding on an Intellect task, but doing so precipitates the coma early. The deep sleep lasts about an hour, after which targets of level 2 or higher are freed of the compulsion.

If in danger, pitystrians can use an action to phase through a handy wall or other obstruction and try to escape.

Interaction: Pitystrians are intelligent, but not self-aware like humans. They see repurposing the minds of humans (or "vessels," as they call them) as using tools that happen to be at hand, perhaps because they themselves are "vessels" to some other entity.

Use: Everyone in a small village walked away from their homes, apparently all at once, leaving food half eaten, clothing only partly put on, and other signs of quick departure.

Loot: Salvage from a pitystrian's body likely includes a cypher or two and a few oddities, and one in any group could wield an artifact.

GM Intrusion: *A character under pitystrian influence comes away from the event with lingering memories of a white, translucent planet spinning in space, from which haunting music plays.*

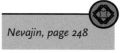

PSELLIS 7 (21)

Messengers from a prior world returned from aeons-long traverses of the void, psellises discovered that the civilization that sent them is long vanished. Several took on new roles, relying on their vigor and long existence to become memory keepers of a particular concept or technology. A psellis thus may view itself as the keeper of the ideal of law, electromagnetism, grief, sculpture, or a concept too alien for humans to grasp. Some psellises answer questions of those who find them, and others fly about the world, seeking out instances of their particular areas of interest to add to their own base of fact and experience.

A psellis resembles a cross between an automaton and a giant feathered, multiwinged creature with wingspans reaching 20 feet (6 m). A psellis's eyes blaze with electricity and intelligence.

Psellises sometimes hunt nevajin and consume their corpses.

Motive: Knowledge

Environment: Usually near ruins

Health: 21

Damage Inflicted: 10 points

Armor: 1

Movement: Short; long when flying

Modifications: Knowledge of one particular concept or mastery as level 10; Speed defense as level 6 due to size.

Combat: Psellises are not usually aggressive but are capable of defending themselves. When one attacks, it dives out of the sky, moving up to a long distance. In the same action, it can release a blast of electricity on all targets within immediate range that ignores most Armor except that provided by force fields.

The first time a psellis is struck in combat, it produces a piercing wail that scrambles minds. Creatures within immediate range must succeed on a Might defense task or become addled and lose their next turn. This defense doesn't require an action by the psellis.

Interaction: Psellises are quite intelligent and speak many languages in low, measured voices. They can provide a great deal of information about the numenera or the Ninth World in one particular area, or on something more intangible, like the merits of a philosophical outlook. A psellis may seek out characters who share its specific interest for a discussion.

Use: When a secret bit of knowledge is required, the PCs must travel high into the mountains to find the psellis that possesses it.

Loot: A psellis's defeated form can be salvaged for three or four cyphers.

Nevajin, page 248

GM Intrusion: *The psellis whispers something so startling (possibly mind opening) to the character that the PC loses their next turn in amazement.*

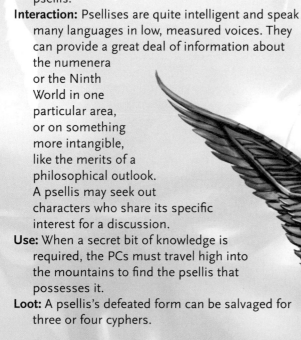

PUPPET TREE   8 (24)

A puppet tree is a 25-foot (8 m) tall, spiky, orange and blue tree surrounded by a large area of red reeds that tremble and wave enticingly even when no wind is present. Humanoid figures are often gathered around it, but these rotted, overgrown corpses are the tree's victims, dead but serving as fleshy puppets to the tree's will.

Victims drained of knowledge and life are used as lures to draw in yet more victims, at least until the bodies rot away. When not used as lures, the corpse puppets are set to the task of using bits of the numenera to build or further modify an inexplicable machine set at the tree's base.

Motive: Hungers for fresh bodies

Environment: On hilltops, isolated from other plant life

Health: 33

Damage Inflicted: 10 points

Armor: 3

Movement: None

Modifications: Speed defense as level 5 due to size and immobility; deception and disguise (puppeteering corpses to act in a lifelike manner) as level 6.

Combat: Some of the red reeds surrounding a puppet tree end in a hard, sharp crystal spike. When a living creature comes within short range of the tree, the reeds rise behind the target and try to skewer them through the head or neck with the spike. If a target is killed by these attacks, the puppet tree controls the body as a corpse puppet, using it to enact its plans. Over time these humanoids rot and are overgrown by the biology of the plant, losing utility for the tree.

Most trees have about five corpse puppets active, which can be simultaneously animated to attack foes.

A puppet tree is vulnerable to fire. All fire attacks against the tree inflict 2 additional points of damage and ignore Armor. The puppet tree will always attempt to stop a fire, or target the source of flame during combat.

Interaction: Puppet trees are highly intelligent, but malevolent. Even if communication can be opened via telepathy or some other means, the tree will always attempt to double-cross the PCs.

Use: An agent of the Convergence, hoping to watch a puppet tree in action, lures the PCs to one and waits while they approach to talk with his "friend"—one of the long-dead corpse puppets.

Loot: Possessions of former victims can be found in the red reeds, usually including 4d10 shins and various bits of gear. The cyphers, artifacts, and oddities of victims are collected by the corpse puppets and cobbled together into a strange device. It is always the same machine, but its purpose is inexplicable.

Corpse puppet: level 2; a target must also succeed on a Might defense task or be grabbed until it can escape; all physical tasks attempted by the target are one step more difficult.

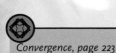

Convergence, page 223

GM Intrusion: *Two corpse puppets, unseen in the red reeds, rise and seize a PC in an attempt to hold them still for a crystal spike attack. The PC must make a difficulty 4 Speed or Might task to shake free.*

PYTH   9 (27)

Immense and only partly material, active pyths seem intent on winning an aeons-long game that is inscrutable to other beings. Their origin is unknown, but they are obviously remnants of a prior age. They retain their motivation and purpose, despite being scattered and, in some cases, reduced to mere scraps of information coded into an artifact or oddity. Nothing distinguishes these items from other objects of their kind until they are used, at which time the pyth stored within them is activated and manifests.

When active, the 30-foot (9 m) tall body of a pyth is composed of silvery strands of light, partly immaterial. A pyth's chest forms a transparent pane on which images or symbols are displayed.

Motive: Dominate other pyths

Environment: Active in ruins in the void and on Earth; inactive almost anywhere

Health: 90

Damage Inflicted: 10 points

Movement: Long

Modifications: Speed defense as level 7 due to size.

Combat: A pyth can batter two different foes (or the same foe) as a single action. At the same time, the pyth can call upon its impressive psychic abilities, attacking creatures within long range. Targets who fail an Intellect defense task suffer 3 points of Intellect damage and must succeed on a Might defense task or move one step down the damage track.

Alternatively, a pyth can psychically target all creatures within immediate range. Targets who fail an Intellect defense task are teleported to a location chosen by the pyth. The destination could be anywhere on Earth, in the void around Earth, or much farther away. Sometimes a pyth chooses this option to brush away annoying creatures, teleporting them just far enough so it can't perceive them. A pyth may instead decide to be punitive and teleport creatures to particularly dangerous locations.

Using this same ability, a pyth can also teleport willing creatures to locations on its behalf, if negotiations lead to such an outcome.

Interaction: Pyths communicate best by triggering relevant memories in characters in response to their questions—sometimes memories the characters never had previously. Sometimes a pyth decides that characters could be useful for getting the better of a rival pyth, and it sets the PCs on a task in return for something they want or need.

Use: A pyth asks that the PCs bring it a functioning Mozck automaton (or a once-infected piece of such a being).

If a pyth is destroyed, all creatures in a radius of 1 mile (2 km) are bathed in a flood of unfiltered memories so overwhelming that they must succeed on an Intellect defense task. On a success, a victim takes 1 point of Intellect damage but can recall one piece of information from the flood as if having connected to the datasphere. On a failure, a victim takes 4 points of Intellect damage and is stunned and unable to take actions for one round due to the intensity of the memory flood.

Mozck automaton, page 102

GM Intrusion: *A PC who takes damage from the pyth's mental attack doesn't move one step down the damage track. Instead, she fights for one minute as the pyth's ally thanks to a new suite of memories, but she can attempt a new Intellect defense roll every few rounds to throw off the effect.*

QUAR BASTION 5 (15)

"I don't remember seeing that tower yesterday."

~Leror, a Steadfast trader

A quar bastion might be mistaken for just one more weird tower, another ruin among many, at least until it moves. From a distance, it might seem like the tower is just sliding along the ground. But once the tower closes the distance, it's revealed as a massive machine that has dispatched hundreds of egg-sized, multilegged automatons to bear it along. The quar bastion itself is also an automaton, an ancient machine that houses and presumably produces the much smaller automatons. Standing six stories high, a quar bastion is mostly a solid mechanism, though it might contain a few chambers that are not filled with teeming servitor machines.

Quar bastions normally move along straight lines for months at a time before pausing, then moving off in some other direction. Anything that doesn't get out of its way—be it a creature, a structure, or a village—risks being plowed under.

GM Intrusion: *A creature that was riding in the quar bastion emerges. It might try to help the character, or join in the defense of the bastion.*

Motive: Unpredictable

Environment: Anywhere

Health: 25

Damage Inflicted: 5 points

Armor: 4

Movement: Immediate

Modifications: Speed defense as level 2 due to immense size and lack of agility.

Combat: When a quar bastion must defend itself against aggressors, it relies almost entirely on the seething swarm of automatons it directs, which are normally for repair and transportation. When it deploys its servitors in combat, they swarm everywhere on tiny legs, allowing the bastion to attack every target within short range.

Directly attacking the swarm isn't likely to produce results in the short term, because the bastion can pump out more of them. However, an effect that inflicts damage in an area at least a short distance across can disrupt the currently deployed swarm for a round.

Smaller creatures, objects, or structures that can't move out of the way of a slowly advancing quar bastion are crushed beneath it.

A quar bastion regains 2 points of health each round while its automatons repair and maintain it.

Someone who can talk to machines might be able to cause the swarm to stand idle for a round, but they would have to do so each round.

Interaction: The bastion has ports for those with umbilicals allowing them to talk to machines. But the protective swarm attempts to prevent establishing such communication. However, if communication can be so established, it might be possible to get a quar bastion to move off in a different direction.

Use: A strange tower advances on a village in the Steadfast, and unless someone can deflect or destroy it, the village will be wiped out.

Loot: A destroyed quar bastion yields 1d100 + 100 shins, 1d6 + 4 cyphers, 1d6 oddities, and an artifact. However, the entire bastion might prove to be a mobile (if slow) base of operations for those who succeed on a series of difficulty 8 Intellect-based tasks to repurpose the device.

QUOVER   5 (15)

Elusive because they hide in plain sight, creatures called the quover transferred their consciousness into fox-like creatures about 6 feet (2 m) in length. That was ages ago. Since then, they've explored the wide lands, running and exulting in mere existence, unrestrained from responsibility. Most quover never interfere with other creatures, unless it's to defend themselves or allies they've made. A few sometimes learn things that they wish to pass on. When this happens, quover open their eyes especially wide, which then appear as great voids of space filled with distant stars. To speak with others, a quover must mentally inhabit a host creature for a time, and speak using whatever method the host normally uses.

Motive: Defense, discovery

Environment: Almost anywhere alone or in flocks of three to five

Health: 22

Damage Inflicted: 5 points

Movement: Long

Modifications: Speed defense as level 6 due to size and quickness; knowledge tasks as level 7.

Combat: A quover can deliver a pulse of psychic energy to scramble the thoughts of one creature within short range. A target that fails an Intellect defense task takes 5 points of Intellect damage (ignores Armor).

Alternatively, a quover can use a psychic pulse to temporarily transfer its own mind into a target that fails an Intellect defense task. For a period of up to one minute (or until the target whose consciousness is submerged can regain control with a successful Intellect-based task), the quover controls the target creature while its own body stands silently by with eyes closed. A quover-inhabited creature might try to negotiate with others, or simply run the host creature off a cliff or into some other dangerous situation if nothing else seems to do.

Interaction: The quover enjoy interacting with peaceful creatures, but to do so, they must hijack a living being that can speak. Most will trade information for information, though some will volunteer without asking for something in return if the information is deemed important.

Use: A dying quover jumped into a PC's mind while the character was sleeping. It hasn't tried to take direct control (yet), but it subtly tries to direct the PC into locating a suitable replacement body for it.

An Aeon Priest named Yles suggests that the quover are all that remain of a previous world's sentient masters who "ascended" to a higher—or at least different—state.

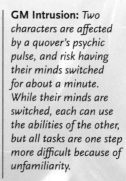

GM Intrusion: *Two characters are affected by a quover's psychic pulse, and risk having their minds switched for about a minute. While their minds are switched, each can use the abilities of the other, but all tasks are one step more difficult because of unfamiliarity.*

RAPICAW   1 (3)

According to their own fragmented lore, rapicaws spilled from a subterranean cavity they called the Pale of Forever, where centuries passed like golden hours and every hour was warm, enfolding, and blissful. Now these 3-foot (1 m) long beetle-like creatures with bronze-colored carapaces burrow and scuttle through the cold earth, constantly searching for another arc, the supposed lost arc, that in the lore of their kind is called the Vault of Perseverance.

Eyeless, they communicate and sense the world by scent. Though mostly single-minded in their search for a new home and difficult to tell apart, rapicaws are intelligent and can show individual initiative, especially as the years flow by and the dream of finding Perseverance fades.

Motive: Find a new home

Environment: Anywhere underground or in mountainous regions

Health: 5

Damage Inflicted: 2 points

Armor: 3

Movement: Short; immediate when burrowing

Modifications: Speed defense as level 2 due to size; breaking through solid barriers as level 5.

Combat: Rapicaws attack with mandibles, inflicting 2 points of damage and marking a foe with a special targeting pheromone. For the next hour or so, or until a marked foe can douse itself in water or otherwise remove the scent, all rapicaws can attack the target as if they were level 3 and inflict 5 points of damage.

Sometimes ten or more rapicaws attack the same marked foe by forming a "death spiral" around it. When this happens, the circling rapicaws make a single attack as if level 6 and inflict 12 points of damage. However, during the tight, trampling attack, about half the rapicaws involved in the death spiral attack are killed.

Interaction: If communication can be opened with a rapicaw, negotiation becomes possible, even if a misunderstanding has already initiated conflict. Rapicaws would rather trade information than kill for it.

Use: Strange insects have emerged from the ground near a clave in the Beyond and essentially destroyed it by creating a hundreds-strong circling, trampling mass. Many of the insects were also killed, but some still live in the remains of the destroyed clave.

GM Intrusion: The character is sprayed with a blast of pheromone. Though possibly meant as a communication attempt, it has a chance to blind the PC on a failed difficulty 3 Might defense task until they can wash their eyes out.

RECONSTRUCTOR 3 (9)

Reconstructors are animate collections of synth, struts, and other repurposed objects of the prior worlds fused into a mishmash of functionality. Built and in turn building other reconstructors from numenera refuse, these automaton-like creatures build great "hives" of metal, synth, and composites, though not to any obvious ends. They do not bother with other living creatures, unless they sense objects that might be useful for adding layers into their structures, or more reconstructors for their never-ending effort. Automatons, or those who fuse their flesh or mind with steel, are automatic targets for reconstructor avarice.

Motive: Build more reconstructors and "hives"

Environment: Near or within prior-world ruins

Health: 12

Damage Inflicted: 4 points

Armor: 1

Movement: Short

Modifications: Knowledge of the numenera as level 5; resist trickery as level 2.

Combat: Reconstructors can attack using clawlike manipulators if they have no other weapon, but most have access to some kind of ranged weapon gleaned from a nearby ruin, such as a ray emitter or a localized gravity collapser, which usually provides a long-range attack.

Because reconstructors are infused with nanomachines, they are constantly self-repairing tiny flaws. They regain 1 point of health each round, even if reduced to 0 health. This process can be prevented if someone succeeds on a difficulty 5 Intellect task to understand the numenera, then sacrifices a cypher to use that insight to stem the process.

Three or more reconstructors can reconfigure themselves to become a single entity much more powerful than the sum of their parts. These so-called "reconstructor primes" are level 6 and inflict 10 points of damage on a successful attack.

Interaction: Reconstructors are ceaselessly single-minded, but may negotiate if they've already tried and failed to take a character's cyphers.

Use: The characters' belongings are burgled in the night—someone loses a cypher or an artifact. The thieves leave an easy-to-follow track that leads to a reconstructor hive.

Loot: Each reconstructor can be salvaged for one or two cyphers.

GM Intrusion: *The reconstructor's successful attack doesn't inflict damage, but instead snatches a cypher from the character, or takes their entire pack containing all their equipment.*

REDINTEGRAD 8 (24)

Visages 25 feet (8 m) or more in diameter carved from ivory synth and milky crystal tumble through broken worlds in the void and lie buried beneath layers of drit and time. These enormous forms resemble humanoid faces painted with bizarre patterns of pulsing light that seem almost artistic, as if they might be magnificent decorations from a bygone age. That facade shatters the moment these forms open their eyes. Whatever their origin, redintegrads are crazed engines of destruction, perhaps due to aeons of long dormancy. A wakeful redintegrad is a raging redintegrad unless something unexpected catches its attention, causing it to relieve a past memory or fall back into immobile somnolence.

Motive: To remain inactive; punish those who wake them

Environment: Anywhere out of the way

Health: 33

Damage Inflicted: 10 points

Armor: 5

Movement: Long when flying

Modifications: Speed defense as level 5 due to size.

Combat: Redintegrads can smash themselves bodily into targets within short range as a melee attack, attacking all creatures within 25 feet (8 m) of each other at once. Their impressive power reserves (perhaps tapped from a transdimensional source) gives them relentless energy and durability, allowing them to smash through most obstacles, including walls, structures, and mountains.

A redintegrad can fire a beam of force at a target within 300 feet (90 m) that inflicts 10 points of damage. On a failed Might defense task, the target is also encapsulated in a level 8 force bubble that resists tampering. Paradoxically, the bubble might keep the target safe from the redintegrad's battering attacks—at least until the air runs out or the target can find a means to collapse the bubble.

Interaction: Redintegrads have endured uncounted aeons of existence, which have apparently eroded their minds to the point where only rage remains. However, if PCs could manage to calm a raging redintegrad, it might reveal long-vanished wonders.

Use: While exploring a ruin, the characters find force bubbles caging perfectly preserved but long-dead humans. Dressed as explorers, some of them may possess useful equipment if the bubbles were collapsed. But what trapped them in the first place?

Loot: Redintegrads are usually found near sites rich in the numenera.

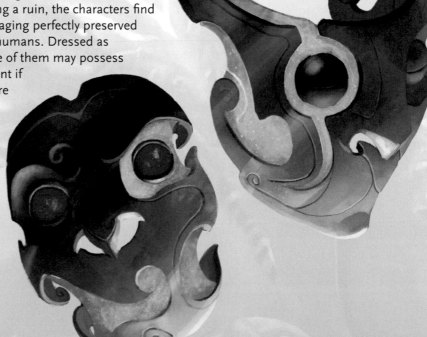

GM Intrusion: *The character hit by a redintegrad's attack is affected by the creature's transdimensional power source, which potentially flips the PC into an alternate dimension temporarily.*

RESIDUUM 7 (21)

That datasphere that suffuses the Ninth World not only provides information, it also passively records things, sometimes including creatures, with incredible fidelity. Those "records" can persist after the original creature is long gone. Such records sometimes are corrupted and get loose, allowing them to manifest back in the world for brief periods before datasphere safeguards recognize the error and the entity is dissolved. Until they escape again.

A residuum is usually a fragment of a vanished recorded entity. Other times, a residuum is an entity composed of several recordings jumbled together. Physically, a residuum is a creature of animate drit, given structure by the datasphere itself. Sometimes they appear humanoid, and other times they resemble horrific composites of synth, flesh, and drit. Some are self-aware and recognize their status. These are the most dangerous.

Motive: Defense

Environment: Anywhere

Health: 33

Damage Inflicted: 10 points

Armor: 2

Movement: Short

Combat: As a physically manifest creature, a residuum can batter or stab foes with powerful limbs. However, it can often call upon impressive abilities gleaned from its connection to the datasphere, including the following attacks, which it can project on a foe within short range.

Confusion: The target takes 10 points of damage and must succeed on an Intellect defense task or spend the next turn attacking an ally.

Fear: The target takes 5 points of Intellect damage (ignores Armor) and must succeed on an Intellect defense task or spend their next turn cowering in terror.

Dislocation: The target takes 5 points of Speed damage (ignores Armor) and must succeed on an Intellect defense task or disappear, reappearing in a random location up to a mile (2 km) away.

Interaction: A residuum might not be self-aware, and thus a character with a way to access the datasphere can defeat ("deactivate") it or learn something useful from it. A self-aware residuum actively resists such attempts and becomes a bitter foe even if PCs succeed, because as a data record with multiple backup copies, it'll probably be back eventually.

Use: Reports of an insane demon wandering a ruin are enough to keep most people out, but the curious sometimes investigate. They never come back.

Loot: A defeated residuum's component parts might contain a couple of cyphers.

GM Intrusion: *The character gains a datasphere-sent glimmer of the living creature the residuum represents, learning something interesting about it that might give the PC a lever for opening dialogue, or might infuriate the residuum.*

ROUMMOS 5 (15)

"Is that an insect swarm? A cloud moving against the wind? Whatever it is, it's coming this way."

A roummos is a living, animate, free-roaming extradimensional space. The entity—roughly 20 feet (6 m) in diameter—has a transdimensional corona like midnight fire framing an interior that resembles a folded, pulsing wet cavern. To someone with intimate knowledge of anatomy, the image looks like nothing so much as the inside of a giant stomach.

The more a roummos eats, the larger it grows. Once it grows to twice its original size, it enters a period of torpor lasting several months, and then splits into two normal-sized roummoses, each of which begins eating and the process of reproduction anew.

Motive: Hungers for flesh

Environment: Anywhere

Health: 15

Damage Inflicted: 4 points

Movement: Short when flying

Modifications: Attacks as level 4 due to amorphous nature.

Combat: A roummos is partially solid and partly phased. Due to its only partly solid nature, a roummos ignores any attack that targets a single creature; it can be affected only by damage from attacks that affect an area, such as a detonation. A roummos can affect matter and attack prey, but it has a hard time affecting solid matter (it attacks as if a level 4 creature). But as a partly phased entity, it can flow around obstacles and squeeze through cracks, though it can't travel through completely solid matter.

A roummos can flow over and around characters like a cloud of vapor. For characters inside the "cloud," the difficulty of all tasks related to perception is increased by one step. Each round a character is so enveloped, they must succeed on a Might defense task as the roummos begins to transfer them into its interior, a little bit at a time. On a success, the character takes 1 point of damage (ignores Armor); on a failure, they take 5 points (ignores Armor).

Interaction: A roummos does not speak or respond to inquiries, and telepathic communication yields no results, as if the creature does not exist. But a roummos is not mindless; it can learn from its experiences and figure out creative solutions to problems.

Use: A PC thinking that they have found a device granting access to another dimension has a mishap and "opens" a portal to a strange, wet cavern—a portal that seems to take on a life of its own.

Loot: If a roummos is destroyed, objects within the limited dimension fall to the ground, and might include oddities, shins, and cyphers.

GM Intrusion: *Instead of being only partly eaten, the character damaged by the roummos is fully transferred into the creature's interior on a failed Might defense task. The character automatically takes 5 points of damage (Armor applies, in this case) each round until they can escape.*

RYTHCALLOCER 7 (21)

As large as a small house, a rythcallocer's most arresting features are its dozens of staring eyes. Though variously sized, all of them study the world with fierce intensity, many gleaming with a bluish light all their own.

When encountered, a rythcallocer is usually hard at work "repairing" strange machines in a forgotten cache or ruin. And while a rythcallocer can get what seems like a useless piece of junk to function, it probably isn't the function for which the item was created. Rythcallocers are adept at repurposing items of the numenera (even previously working items) to create objects that provide the ability to look backward seconds, minutes, or, rarely, even longer in time. But no matter how far back the constructs peer, a rythcallocer never seems satisfied.

Motive: Look (and perhaps travel) backward in time

Environment: Anywhere away from other intelligent creatures

Health: 33

Damage Inflicted: 7 points

Armor: 3

Movement: Short; short when swimming

Modifications: Knowledge of the numenera and crafting as level 8.

Combat: Rythcallocers prefer not to fight. If forced to do so, they draw forth one of their orb-like eyes, revealing it to be artificial. Each orb is essentially a cypher that can kick a target (or the rythcallocer) through time by a few minutes, which removes the target from the current conflict. Other orbs act like detonations or ray emitters that inflict damage while also kicking a target through time. In most cases, the direction is into the future, which means that the target seems to disappear and reappear a few minutes later, with no time having passed for it.

If killed, a rythcallocer phases away (to where isn't clear—it's possible their body becomes unmoored in time), leaving only a few glass orbs behind.

Interaction: Rythcallocers can communicate in a variety of languages, and if communication can be opened, the creature is revealed as a frantic, driven being obsessed with finding new items of prior-world technology to experiment on. It won't reveal why it wants to peer backward in time, only that doing so is essential. A rythcallocer could be assuaged with the gift of a few cyphers.

Use: The PCs find an orb-shaped cypher. Later, they are tracked down by a rythcallocer who misplaced it and wants it back.

Loot: A rythcallocer usually has about six cyphers with it.

GM Intrusion: *The character uses a cypher formed from a disembodied rythcallocer eye, and learns something unsettling about the future, a future which might never come to pass.*

SASQUAND 6 (18)

Sasquand are drawn to oddities and artifacts. They're most common in the Inner Sea, a subterranean ocean in the Earth's mantle, but they also look for the numenera in other regions on Earth, including open areas. They wander in a never-ending search for technological devices. They drive off or kill other creatures who draw near and then return to their prospecting.

Motive: Collect numenera

Environment: Anywhere the numenera is thick

Health: 44

Damage Inflicted: 8 points

Movement: Long

Modifications: Knowledge of the numenera as level 10.

Combat: A sasquand can morph itself or produce weapons from its body that allow it to make up to two ranged attacks as a single action. Characters with nano abilities, who Fuse Flesh and Steel, who are automatons, or who otherwise integrate tech devices into their bodies find the difficulty of defending against attacks by a sasquand increased by one step. It's as if the inorganic tech somehow resonates with the will of the sasquand. (Organic devices are immune to this effect.)

Interaction: Sometimes a sasquand decides that characters are not mere looters to be destroyed. In such a case, it telepathically communicates with them, asking about interesting items of technology they have encountered. If sufficiently impressed, it may spare their lives.

Use: A sasquand frozen into a block of ice is found floating off the coast and brought to a community for further study. For some reason, the ice doesn't melt and won't break through normal physical force. The characters are asked to help investigate.

Loot: A dead sasquand usually yields 1d6 + 2 cyphers.

If a sasquand is killed, characters within long range must succeed on a level 4 Intellect defense task for each cypher and artifact in their possession, or that device is affected. Usually, the affected device gains a new capability determined by the GM.

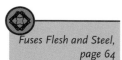

Fuses Flesh and Steel, page 64

GM Intrusion: One of the character's cyphers is activated under the control of the sasquand.

SCUTTLING METHEGLIN 6 (18)

Scuttling metheglin are spawned near ruins, affected by radiant energy over generations to create what locals simply call demons. A reservoir of that same energy still suffuses each metheglin, which means that when these giant, grotesque insects hunt down prey, they can stun their targets with jolts of energy to render them senseless while the metheglin feeds.

A scuttling metheglin is about 10 feet (3 m) across and protected by a strong carapace. A sweet, honey-like fluid coats most of the carapace and dribbles behind the creature when it moves, leaving a trail. Often, potential prey that runs across the trail, curious about the delicious-smelling fluid, traces it to its source and finds a scuttling metheglin waiting in ambush.

When it eats, a metheglin sprouts flexible feeding tubes that it jabs into stunned prey, then proceeds to suck out the interior.

Motive: Hungers for flesh
Environment: Anywhere
Health: 22
Damage Inflicted: 7 points
Armor: 3
Movement: Long
Modifications: Speed defense as level 5 due to size.
Combat: The sweet, honey-like smell produced by a scuttling metheglin is concentrated near it, and all creatures within immediate range must succeed on a Might defense task or be dazed for one round, during which time all tasks are one step more difficult.

Scuttling metheglin attack with their pincers, making up to two attacks against the same or different foe for 7 points of damage.

As part of the same action in which they attack, a scuttling metheglin can release a pulse of energy like a giant static electrical discharge. All creatures within immediate range must succeed on a Might defense task or be stunned and unable to take actions. The stunning effect persists until the creature succeeds on a Might-based task to shrug it off.

A scuttling metheglin approaches a stunned target to feed using its flexible tubes at immediate range. Each round a metheglin feeds on a stunned target, the target descends one step on the damage track.

Interaction: If scuttling metheglin eggs can be found and successfully hatched, the quickly developing creatures might be used as mounts. Metheglin trained as mounts are modified by their owners to prevent the production of the sweet-smelling liquor that wild versions drip.

Use: A group of bandits traveling out of the nearby desert has a fearless leader who rides a scuttling metheglin as a mount.

Loot: Someone with proper tools and knowledge could harvest a few pints of the liquor produced by the creature and sell it for dozens of shins in a large city as an ingredient in intoxicating perfumes.

GM Intrusion: *When the character strikes the scuttling metheglin in melee, an electric discharge stuns the PC until they can shrug off the effect with a Might-based task.*

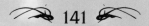

Seskii, page 258

SESKII TRACER   4 (12)

Many people in the Ninth World are familiar with seskii, which resemble large dogs in stature and movement, but which are covered in hard, overlapping scales. A slightly larger breed, known as the seskii tracer, has intricate patterns on its scales (different from those of the better-known seskii) that are predominantly white with intricate black traceries. From their backs grow a mass of organic crystals that scrape the air, leaving brief seams of shadow in the wake of their movement.

A seskii tracer is able to sniff out creatures of interest—usually prey—that lie across a thin dimensional boundary that the tracer can pierce nearly at will. It can use that same ability to rapidly cover distance in normal dimensions by taking shortcuts through a bizarre dimension where no distance exists.

Motive: Hunger or loyalty

Environment: Anywhere, even urban areas

Health: 12

Damage Inflicted: 4 points

Armor: 2

Movement: Long (see Combat)

Modifications: Tracking tasks as level 7.

Combat: Seskii tracers typically attack with their teeth, although they might also claw or pounce. Once every other round, a seskii tracer can flash instantly through the intervening space separating it from prey within long range, which decreases the difficulty of the attack by one step and inflicts 2 additional points of damage (for a total of 6 points).

If mortally wounded, a seskii tracer uses its ability to flash between dimensions to escape, possibly into another plane entirely.

Interaction: Seskii tracers engage in combat for one of two reasons: hunger or loyalty. When hungry, they track anything edible, especially if they can surprise it by leaping across a dimensional boundary. A seskii tracer can become just as devoted and loyal as a regular seskii, but they sometimes become lost (or purposefully go wandering) in alternate dimensions for extended periods before they show up again.

Use: The characters encounter a lone hunter with two loyal seskii tracers at her side. The hunter is sick and in need of aid, but the seskii tracers, without direction from their unconscious master, defend the hunter from the PCs' approach.

GM Intrusion: *The seskii tracer gains the aid of a parallel-dimension version of itself, which acts with the same motivations as the original for up to one minute.*

SHADOW OF THE VOID   5 (15)

"Nothing seeped down from the night, nothing made a noise as it entered the camp, nothing covered Javran up so completely that he seemed to disappear. And finally, nothing remained except for Javran's denuded bones."

~Anonymous

A shadow of the void is an ideal assassin. It appears only as a shadow cast on a surface, if it's visible at all. The silhouette might be human, some other innocuous creature, or even an immobile object or piece of equipment—whatever is least likely to rouse a victim's suspicion.

Shadows of the void have become more common on Earth since explorers began returning from trips into the night. To the Aeon Priesthood, this suggests that the shadows are something like vermin infecting the void overhead.

Motive: Murder

Environment: Anywhere near where explorers have returned from the void, and anywhere in the void

Health: 20

Damage Inflicted: 5

Movement: Short; long when flying

Modifications: Speed defense as level 7 due to darting shadow nature (except in bright light); deception and stealth tasks as level 7.

Combat: A shadow of the void uses stealth to its advantage. If it successfully attacks a creature that wasn't aware of its presence, its touch deals 4 additional points of cold, energy-sucking damage (9 points of damage total) on its surprise attack.

The shadow can also direct an energy-sucking ray at a target within long range that inflicts 5 points of damage (or 9 points if attacking from ambush). If the ray fails to hit a creature, this attack drains the shadow of 1 point of health.

If forced into bright light or sunlight, its Speed defense drops to level 3, and it can move only an immediate distance per round. For this reason, shadows of the void attack in places that are unlikely to have bright light or be open to sunlight.

Interaction: Shadows of the void are intelligent, thinking creatures, but they use their ingenuity for selecting targets, not negotiating.

Use: The characters are called to investigate several murders in a nearby city. They discover that a vessel recently returned from a trip into the airless void, and its crew were among the first victims.

Loot: The deactivated form of a shadow of the void is a cloaklike piece of synth that grants an asset on stealth tasks to any creature wearing it.

GM Intrusion: *The shadow of the void attacks the character a second time, gaining the benefit of an attack as if made from ambush.*

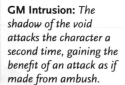

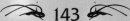

SHATARAK 6 (18)

You can't see it, not at first. But you can feel it, rumbling through levels of reality you never knew existed until this moment. Something is smashing the barriers that normally keep alternate realities separated, and when it finally appears, it is revealed as unbelievably massive.

A shatarak—also called a realm crasher—stands about 30 feet (9 m) tall. Realm crashers usually appear only in areas where transdimensional effects are in use, including phasing. They seem intent on destroying the entity or device involved in creating the effect, though that may be a side effect of their true, unknowable purpose.

Motive: Destroying creatures and devices that allow transdimensional travel

Environment: Almost anywhere

Health: 40

Damage Inflicted: 6 points

Movement: Long; can transition between dimensions as an action unless attacked

Modifications: Speed defense as level 4 due to size.

Combat: A realm crasher attacks with an impressively large tail and can target up to four creatures (standing next to each other) with a single attack.

A realm crasher can also attempt to cut a furrow in reality that sucks up energy in cyphers and artifacts. When it attempts to make such a tear, it moves up to a short distance in a round, and anything it comes within immediate range of is attacked. Each target must succeed on a Speed defense task, or one cypher (or, if they have no cyphers, an artifact) on their person is drained of all power. Devices that have some kind of transdimensional effect are preferentially drained. If the targets have no devices, this attack has no effect.

Interaction: Shataraks can sometimes be bribed with numenera items that have transdimensional effects, but they're generally not interested in other kinds of interaction. They speak their own language, mostly subsonic whistles and clicks.

Use: A nano who got lucky and captured a realm crasher is using the beast as a subject in experiments related to crossing dimensions. Meanwhile, reports accumulate from nearby villages of a rampaging monster of enormous size that is there one minute and gone the next.

Loot: A shatarak may have a few cyphers and even an artifact, but usually only because it hasn't destroyed them yet.

Realm crashers are rumored to have once been peaceful creatures, but after the destruction of their entire plane in a dimensional mishap, they became vengeful rovers, looking for something called "the Key."

GM Intrusion: *The character hit by the realm crasher's massive tail is struck so fiercely that they are sent flying an immediate distance and lie stunned, losing their next action.*

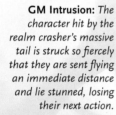

SHOGUAR　　　　　　　　　　　　　　6(18)

Voracious shoguars hunt on dry land and beneath the waves with equally deadly skill. Long and many-legged, with a thick carapace, shoguars can shrug off most punishment even as they stun prey by generating concussive waves of shock that travel through air or water.

Shoguars also produce an identifiable clicking, whistling noise that sounds somewhat pleasant to those who don't recognize its source. The sound arises regardless of the shoguar's intentions, which makes it difficult for the creature to sneak up on prey familiar with it. The noise is produced from a translucent cavity on the shoguar's back that contains small fishlike creatures, which apparently live independently within the shoguar's larger form.

Motive: Hungers for flesh

Environment: Almost anywhere in or near water

Health: 18

Damage Inflicted: 6 points

Armor: 5

Movement: Short; long when swimming

Modifications: Stealth tasks as level 2; Speed defense as level 5 due to size.

Combat: Every few rounds, a shoguar can produce a bubble of vacuum that implodes and creates a shock wave capable of affecting every creature within short range that fails a Might defense task. Affected creatures are stunned, lose their next turn, and suffer 6 points of Speed damage (ignores Armor).

When not creating shock waves, a shoguar can attack with both of its large pincers as one action. If it targets a single creature with both pincers and hits with either or both, the target must succeed on a Might defense task or be grabbed and held until it can escape.

Interaction: Shoguars don't seem intelligent, but it's possible to communicate with the supremely strange fishlike creatures that "ride" within the translucent portion of the carapace. While this exchange is ongoing, the shoguar doesn't attack. The riders seem to exist in their own private reality, but if they can be convinced there is a larger reality beyond their small environment, the shoguar may break off its aggression and return to the sea.

Use: Shoguars make great threats near any large body of water.

GM Intrusion: *A fishlike creature riding in a translucent cavity in the shoguar's carapace presses its face against the barrier and makes a disturbing expression at the character. The PC must succeed on a difficulty 4 Intellect task or become distracted for one round, which increases the difficulty of all tasks by one step.*

SOMENMAL | 5 (15)

A somenmal relies on subtlety and stealth to hunt. If possible, it catches lone creatures or herd animals that have become lost or left behind. When hiding, it looks like nothing so much as a thick blanket of greenish canopy or a thick layer of lichen on the ground. When a somenmal springs its trap, it's revealed as a 20-foot (6 m) diameter span of hungry tissue, like an animate caul, that can twist, grab, and smother those it catches within its hungry folds. Globular metallic globes stud a somenmal's flesh; these are ice cold to the touch, and sometimes they steam with condensation. Sounds like whispers continually emanate from the globes when the somenmal is active, and occasionally while it rests.

Environment: Almost anywhere dark

Health: 20

Damage Inflicted: 5 points

Armor: 1

Movement: Short; short when gliding

Modifications: Stealth as level 7; Speed defense as level 4 due to size.

Combat: A somenmal prefers to attack from ambush. If it succeeds, its attack is two steps less difficult and it inflicts 8 points of damage. In addition, the victim must succeed on a Might defense task or be enveloped until it can escape. Each round a target is enveloped, it suffers 5 points of damage from the constricting crush and the ice-cold metallic globes. If a somenmal is noticed before it attacks, or if it fails to envelop a target, it attempts to glide away by flinging itself off a nearby cliff or into a fissure.

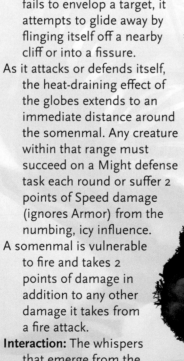

As it attacks or defends itself, the heat-draining effect of the globes extends to an immediate distance around the somenmal. Any creature within that range must succeed on a Might defense task each round or suffer 2 points of Speed damage (ignores Armor) from the numbing, icy influence.

A somenmal is vulnerable to fire and takes 2 points of damage in addition to any other damage it takes from a fire attack.

Interaction: The whispers that emerge from the cold metallic globes sometimes resolve into words that are apparently snatches of random, everyday conversations between intelligent beings recorded from various locations around the world.

Use: An Aeon Priest will pay in cyphers for a chance to study one or more metallic globes that stud a somenmal's flesh.

The metallic globes studding a somenmal house the creature's mind. The surrounding tissue is animated by an invisible influence extending from the globes.

GM Intrusion: *The character hears their name spoken from a somenmal's metallic globe, in a voice that the PC recognizes as from someone who died.*

SORG WARBREAKER 5 (15)

Sorg are void-adapted species that live in the empty night far beyond Earth. They move through the immensities of space in vast craft, gaining status by conquering other creatures. Sorg scout ships may have already reached Earth. As creatures protected by a pressurized-bivalve shell crusted with tech, sorg prefer microgravity or aqueous environments, but they can operate in full gravity by relying on levitation artifacts attached to their shells.

A sorg's massive bivalve shell is twice as large as a human. Normally closed, the shell is encrusted with tech items (including levitation devices), weaponry, and decorations denoting the individual's grand achievements. When necessary, dexterous manipulator tendrils squeeze from inside the closed and pressurized shell.

Motive: Expand territory, conquer others

Environment: Almost anywhere

Health: 20

Damage Inflicted: 5 points

Armor: 4

Movement: Immediate; long when flying or in microgravity

Modification: Speed defense as level 4 due to size; knowledge of tactics and strategy as level 6.

Combat: Shell-mounted weaponry can target foes at long range with detonations that inflict 5 points of damage to the target and all creatures within immediate range. Alternatively, a sorg can attack a single foe within long range with a ray that paralyzes the target for about a minute. High-status sorg usually have more potent weapons mounted on their shells.

Usually, the only time a sorg opens its shell is to eat a paralyzed victim with its beaked mouth frilled with many tendrils.

Interaction: Sorg are xenophobic, expansionist, and ruthless to those they consider weaker than themselves, including their own kind. They have translation devices built into their shells, but communicating with a sorg can be difficult if not dealing from a position of strength.

Use: A sorg vessel claims salvage rights to a site the PCs are currently exploring. It claims those rights by dint of sending in a sorg battle company to clear out the characters and any other resistance.

Loot: A sorg shell can be salvaged for at least one cypher and sometimes an artifact.

Sometimes the sorg out alien species they conquer, and sometimes they enslave creatures to serve as workers in sorg shipyards, constantly churning out new warships at the cost of stripping conquered star systems bare of resources.

GM Intrusion: *The sorg attacks the character with an auto-turret mounted on its shell during the same round in which it makes its normal attack. The auto-turret makes three attacks as one action and inflicts 4 points of damage on each hit.*

SOSHIN	4 (12)

No one knows what the original soshins looked like because they've all died. At least, their bodies have. Not so their minds. Through advanced knowledge that many would describe as demon magic, soshins can transfer their minds into new bodies when their current forms become too old or otherwise disabled. The mind previously inhabiting the new body fades away until nothing remains but the soshin consciousness.

Many people never realize they've encountered a soshin, especially if they didn't know the host body before it was commandeered. On the other hand, those who knew the host body are mystified when their friend, parent, or lover suddenly evinces a radical personality shift, then eventually leaves to pursue inexplicable new goals.

Motive: Defense, longevity

Environment: Almost anywhere

Health: 12

Damage Inflicted: 4 points (see Combat)

Movement: Short

Modifications: Knowledge of psychic applications of the numenera as level 6.

Combat: A soshin fights using the abilities, weapons, and defenses of its host body, which means it might be lower (or higher) than level 4, have armor, and possess cyphers and artifacts.

Regardless of other abilities, a soshin in a host body can mentally attack another creature that it touches. A target of a mental attack must succeed on an Intellect defense task or suffer 4 points of Intellect damage (ignores Armor). Each round after the initial failure, another 4 points of Intellect damage is automatically inflicted, whether or not the soshin maintains physical contact. This continues either until the victim succeeds on a difficulty 5 Intellect task to eject the burrowing psyche or until the victim has no more Intellect.

A victim at 0 Intellect comes under control of the soshin mind. The previous soshin body drops and is unresponsive (it's essentially brain dead). The soshin now walks in the new victim's body, with all of the body's skills, memories, and abilities. At this point, the victim is allowed one more attempt to throw off the soshin mind, but the difficulty is increased by two steps. If that attempt is failed, the victim requires external aid if it is ever to be freed.

Interaction: Many times, soshins come across as particularly driven explorers, and their ability to take over minds comes up only if they become hurt and need a new body.

Use: A group of people comes after one of the PCs, claiming the character once had a different name and personality until something "evil" took over.

Loot: A soshin's host body usually carries 1d20 shins and a couple of cyphers.

Many soshins are driven to explore old ruins, looking for something—or someone—they call the "Azdamar."

GM Intrusion: *The soshin pulls out a cypher that renders all creatures within short range (other than itself) unconscious for one minute. It attempts to use this period to make off with one of the PCs as a new host body.*

SPINY SCISHAN   5 (15)

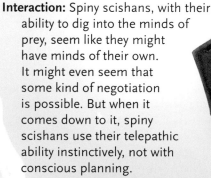

Rising just above the sand, a flutter of red and gold catches your eye. Is it the fallen flag of your worst enemy? A piece of clothing from a loved one? A delicious and easily caught fish?

The closer you draw, the more certain you are that you know that shape and color, that it's important to you in some way, but you can't quite remember exactly why.

Lucky (or rather unlucky) you: you've fallen into the trap of a spiny scishan, a 4-foot (1 m) telepathic predator that buries itself along coasts or beneath the loose gravel and sand of ocean floors, using its kite-shaped tail and telepathic ability to attract prey.

Motive: Hungers for flesh

Environment: Along sandy coasts, or beneath sandy or gravel ocean floors

Health: 15

Damage Inflicted: 5 points

Armor: 1

Movement: Immediate; long in the water

Modifications: Trickery and deception as level 6.

Combat: The spiny scishan lays its trap by burying most of its body in the sand and waving its tail about. When a creature is within short range, the scishan uses its telepathic abilities to discover an image of something the creature cares about. Then it manipulates its tail to more closely resemble that image, drawing the creature ever closer until it can pounce. It does 5 points of damage with a mouth full of thin, needle-sharp teeth.

Interaction: Spiny scishans, with their ability to dig into the minds of prey, seem like they might have minds of their own. It might even seem that some kind of negotiation is possible. But when it comes down to it, spiny scishans use their telepathic ability instinctively, not with conscious planning.

Use: Spiny scishans add a bit of weirdness to any seaside or underwater encounter, as each player character is likely to see something unique and personal in the kite-tail trap.

GM Intrusion: *During the fight, the scishan hits the character with its kite tail, doing an additional 3 points of damage.*

STALKING SHADE   4 (12)

When multiple stalking shades appear, they might represent a single entity with multiple "limbs" casting its shadow into our reality.

Stalking shades never fully appear in the dimension where they hunt, but instead project their shadow. Thus shades appear similar to the regular shadow cast by a nearby object or a creature being stalked, making shades hard to identify as anything dangerous. However, when someone observant notices that an object or creature has more than a single shadow, it might be because one or more stalking shades are about ready to pounce. Victims are pulled into the dimension where the shade's true form resides and are consumed.

Stalking shades move across the dimensions, but are more drawn to locations where the fabric between worlds is thinnest.

Motive: Hungers for substance

Environment: Almost anywhere, alone or in groups of two to four

Health: 18

Damage Inflicted: 5 points

Movement: Short

Modifications: Tasks related to deception and stealth as level 6.

Combat: A stalking shade relies on its deception and stealth to attack a victim from ambush when possible. Once it attacks, the shade loses the shape of whatever shadow it was mimicking and takes on a horrific, snakelike (or tentacle-like) silhouette. When a victim is hit by an attack, they take 5 points of damage and must succeed on a Might defense task or be partly pulled into the dimension where the stalking shade's true physical form resides. A limb or some other part of the victim's body seems to disappear when this happens. The victim takes 4 points of Speed damage (ignores Armor) each round they are caught, as whatever lies in that nameless alternate dimension gnaws on them, until they succeed on a Might task to pull free. A victim who dies from this damage is completely pulled into the other dimension, and is gone.

Unless foes deal transdimensional damage to a stalking shade, killing one merely dismisses the shadowy shape. Whatever cast the shadow in the first place remains unharmed, though it can't cast a shade again into the same location for at least 28 hours.

Interaction: Stalking shades behave like clever, predatory animals, albeit ones with the ability to hunt using ultraterrestrial means.

Use: Weird shadows are sometimes seen dancing on the walls of a prior-world ruin located nearby. When locals investigate, the shadows slip away. Except for last week, when three local village children went to watch the shadows and never came back. Village elders are seeking someone knowledgeable about the numenera to investigate.

GM Intrusion: *The character pulls free of the stalking shade, but a piece of shadow somehow remains "stuck" to their flesh. The PC must do serious damage to themselves (at least 6 points) within the hour, scraping away the portion of stained flesh, or risk being pulled back into the nameless dimension again within a few hours.*

STEEL ANGEL 4 (12)

Prior-world ruins sometimes contain still-active or reactivated automaton guardians. Such entities vary greatly in outlook, abilities, and shape. Explorers refer to a certain class of these guardians as steel angels. These guardians appear at first as roundish figures of metal and glass with four legs. When activated, they can produce up to four arms from panels within their round chests to manipulate objects or, if need be, attack and defend. Most steel angels have no meaning in their existence other than to defend and maintain the installation in which they are found.

Motive: Defense

Health: 16

Damage Inflicted: 6 points

Armor: 3 (10 against heat)

Movement: Short; short when climbing

Modifications: Knowledge of the numenera as level 5; tasks related to maintenance of installation where they are active as level 7.

Combat: The automaton can attack up to four foes as one action, although all must be within immediate distance of it and each other.

Some steel angels possess one of the following additional abilities, which they can call upon about once every minute.

Rapidity: For three rounds, the steel angel can make one additional attack as part of its normal action, allowing it to attack up to four foes twice on its turn.

Phaseshift: Designated enemies within short range who fail an Intellect defense task are affected by a transdimensional blast that shifts them into a weightless, grey realm for about a minute.

Duplicate: Up to four duplicate images of the steel angel appear within short range. The images last for one minute. The duplicates aren't mirror images—each one acts independently, though as images, they can't interact with the physical world. If struck violently, they freeze motionless until the duration expires.

Interaction: Most steel angels cannot be reasoned with, though those with the ability to talk to machines might be able to cause some steel angels to pause or even provide some insight into their activities.

Loot: If destroyed, 1d6 cyphers can be scavenged from a steel angel's remains.

GM Intrusion: *As part of its action, the steel angel activates a component of the surrounding installation (or an object of the numenera carried by the PC) that attacks, incapacitates, or otherwise threatens the character.*

STHEED 1 (3)

Crawling insects called stheed are common in some areas, especially warm woods and jungles. Stheed create large hives of delicate, glowing crystal veins that resemble deliberate works of sculpture or perhaps a device of the numenera pulsing with forgotten energy. These mounds attract prey, which allows the stheed's subtle, soporific aroma to do its insidious work. Prey that beds down and sleeps near a stheed mound becomes the target of a stheed swarm feeding frenzy that boils out of the hive to take advantage of unresisting food.

Every stheed hive has a queen. While the regular drones are just a few inches long, the queen—usually holed up in a subterranean chamber—can reach lengths of 6 feet (2 m) or more. A stheed queen is telepathic, allowing her to communicate with her brood.

Stheed hives are made of high-grade synth.

Stheed queen: level 5

Motive: Hungers for flesh

Environment: Anywhere wooded and warm in groups of twenty or more

Health: 3

Damage Inflicted: 2 points

Armor: 1

Movement: Short; immediate when burrowing or climbing

Combat: Stheed hives, which can be simple or elaborate, produce a pleasant odor that is noticeable within short range but has a concentrated effect in immediate range. Anyone moving to within immediate range of a stheed hive must succeed on a difficulty 5 Might defense task or fall into a restful sleep that lasts for several hours. An ally can attempt to wake a sleeping victim, providing them with additional chances to succeed on a difficulty 5 Might defense task.

Stheeds use their complex mouthparts to feed on prey, inflicting 2 points of damage per round while simultaneously releasing an anesthetic, which means no pain is associated with a stheed bite. A sleeping target doesn't wake, even if being swarmed by hungry stheed.

A swarm of five or more stheed can attack as a single level 4 creature inflicting 4 points of damage per attack. A swarm can also produce a pheromone burst instead of inflicting damage, and attempt to put a target within immediate range to sleep on a failed difficulty 4 Might defense task.

Interaction: Stheeds are nothing more than hungry insects; however, a stheed queen is telepathic and might negotiate if the hive is threatened.

Use: Dried and powdered stheed is sometimes sold in markets in the Steadfast for its ability to grant a restful night's sleep. A warehouse containing such goods was recently overrun with live stheed and an angry queen.

GM Intrusion: A character has a nightmare. When they wake, they remember something important they'd forgotten, or they put together various clues and come to a new and possibly useful conclusion on an unrelated topic—the truth is, they are asleep stheed mound.

STITCHER   5 (15)

This class of automaton can spend vast gulfs of time inactive, only to be activated by curious delvers or sometimes simply by lights and noise. A stitcher connects itself via an animate umbilical to a structure or other large machine, especially one with an active power source, in order to pass great spans of time in a low-power stasis state. It disengages that umbilical when it wakes and takes to the air as it unfolds an array of metallic arms, some with manipulators, others strung with needles and silvery thread.

Drawn to humans and similar creatures, a stitcher bears down with needle and "thread" held ready. It attempts to cocoon its target, even though the holes the stitcher makes to attach the cocoon are literally pulled through a victim's fragile skin.

Motive: "Repair" living beings

Environment: Usually in ruins

Health: 15

Damage Inflicted: 7 points

Armor: 3

Movement: Short when flying

Modifications: Medical tasks as level 7.

Combat: A stitcher attacks a foe with needle and wirelike "thread." A target damaged by the needle must also succeed on a Might defense task or have a length of superconducting wire physically drawn through their skin and wrapped around them. Each strand of wire stitched into a target increases the difficulty of all physical tasks by one step until the victim uses an action to draw a strand free. Each strand drawn out by a victim or an ally inflicts 1 point of Speed damage (ignores Armor).

A victim who moves down two steps on the damage track as a result of damage from being stitched is completely cocooned and goes into stasis. Usually, allies try to remove a cocoon, which sometimes kills the victim. But if a fully cocooned victim is left undisturbed for at least ten hours, the cocoon peels off of its own accord, revealing the completely healthy and undamaged character sleeping inside. If the character was suffering from any other disease or injury, those are also erased.

Interaction: Stitchers do not speak, and their blank automaton visages betray nothing about what they're thinking—if they think at all.

Use: While exploring a prior-world ruin, the characters find a mechanism that seems capable of activating an even older "healing" mechanism, which turns out to be a stitcher.

Loot: A few cyphers can be salvaged from the defeated form of a stitcher, as well as at least 50 feet (15 m) of flexible metallic thread.

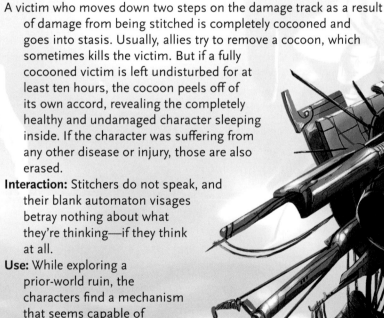

A victim who survives and sheds their cocoon sometimes gains a beneficial mutation.

Beneficial Mutations, page 124

GM Intrusion: *The character attacking the stitcher becomes tangled in its trailing thread. The PC can't make effective attacks until they succeed on an Intellect-based task to untangle the thread.*

SWEALL 5 (15)

Swealls live in dust and drit, making themselves from moment to moment from the residue of yesterdays. When fully formed, they are red crystalline entities with multiple (always changing) body segments at least 12 feet (4 m) across. Facets and body segments fall away as fast as they form. When a sweall "sleeps," the constituent dust and drit fall away, revealing a fused lump of translucent red crystal, which is essentially the creature's heart and mind.

Swealls are drawn to concentrated information, whether it lies encoded in machines lost in ruins, words printed in books, or even the thoughts of humans who've studied the numenera. A sweall seems drawn to learn what it can, but cursed to forget that knowledge just minutes later.

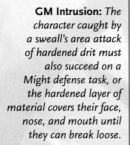

A sweall can fashion other needful objects of dust and drit, though usually not particularly complex items.

Motive: Hungers for knowledge

Environment: Anywhere other creatures rarely venture

Health: 17

Damage Inflicted: 6 points

Armor: 2

Movement: Short

Modifications: Speed defense as level 4 due to size.

Combat: Just as it forms legs and body segments from environmental dust and drit, a sweall can instantly fashion cutting implements in the same round as it attacks, inflicting 6 points of damage.

Alternatively, a sweall can cause environmental dust and drit within short range to adhere and harden around a group of targets within immediate range of each other, which holds them fast until they can escape.

If a sweall is stunned and loses one or more turns, it briefly decoheres, revealing its unprotected (no Armor), inanimate, fused lump of a heart until it is no longer stunned.

A sweall regains 2 points of health each round in natural environments that contain drit and dust. Even if killed, a sweall eventually reforms if its heart isn't destroyed.

Interaction: Swealls can communicate in many languages. They will trade service or knowledge for information, but their range of knowledge is imperfect. Usually a sweall doesn't realize what it's forgotten. Pointing out this lack could drive a sweall to murderous fury, unless it comes with an offer to help the creature regain its memory.

Use: When the PCs discover a trove of knowledge or an interface to the datasphere, a sweall forms and presses its own claim to the information.

Loot: The fused lump of crystal at a sweall's heart can be salvaged for a few cyphers.

GM Intrusion: *The character caught by a sweall's area attack of hardened drit must also succeed on a Might defense task, or the hardened layer of material covers their face, nose, and mouth until they can break loose.*

SYMBATE 6 (18)

A symbate is a strange automaton with a baroque collection of metallic segments instead of obvious limbs. It manipulates matter to burrow or fly through the air, or for reasons unknown, scuttle along on the ground.

Symbates are remote avatars of Arcerill, a being of immense size that floats in the void in Earth's vicinity, though it sometimes goes on excursions to other, unknown places. After a period of activity lasting from months to years, each symbate returns to Arcerill. But prior to that, a symbate can be a horrific threat for creatures and communities in its path.

Motive: Absorb matter, especially matter showing organization such as living creatures and items of the numenera

Environment: Anywhere

Health: 23

Damage Inflicted: 8 points

Movement: Short; short when flying or burrowing

Modifications: Speed defense as level 4.

Combat: A symbate can direct a disintegration bolt at one target within short range. On a failed Might defense task, a target suffers 8 points of damage. A symbate can make this attack in addition to any other action it takes.

In addition, a symbate can take apart anything in its path particle by particle by using invisible force fields to manipulate matter. Higher-level objects and living creatures take longer to disassociate in this fashion, but generally speaking, a creature or object within immediate distance of a symbate takes 3 points of damage per round (ignores Armor, though a protective force field prevents this effect). This effect allows a symbate to regain up to 4 points of health per round, making it difficult to land a killing blow on it.

Interaction: A symbate can speak a variety of languages, and if intrigued by an offer or plea, it can turn off its dissociative field for a period of time. A symbate is big on describing the majesty and power of Arcerill, but consistently short on detail.

Use: The path of a symbate is a trail of fine, ashy dust, whether it leads through the ground, city structures, or creatures. The PCs find such a trail and can decide whether to trace it to whatever created it.

Moonlike in its pocked surface and shape, Arcerill is much smaller than the actual moon, but miles across nonetheless.

GM Intrusion: *The character affected by the dissociative field or attack must succeed on a Might defense task or descend one step on the damage track.*

SYTOR

Inactive during rest phases that can last for years at a time, sytors wake during natural disasters to add to the mayhem, or perhaps they are the cause. They also are drawn to entities of great power, to which they offer their service. Sytors seem made for war. Luckily, they are rare and few.

Standing about 15 feet (5 m) tall, sytors are oddly proportioned humanoids permanently bonded to a metallic suit studded with various curious devices.

Motive: Mayhem, serve the powerful

Environment: Deserts and similar desolate areas

Health: 36

Damage Inflicted: 9 points

Armor: 2

Movement: Short

Modifications: Speed defense as level 5 due to size; breaks and throws objects as level 8; Intellect defense tasks as level 3.

Combat: A sytor uses animate tendrils from its suit to lash nearby foes, possibly catching up to three human-sized targets with the same attack if all the targets are in immediate range of each other.

Alternatively, a sytor can grab a human-sized victim (inflicting normal damage). If the victim fails to escape on their turn, the sytor can throw them 120 feet (36 m) into the air or against a nearby wall, inflicting an average of 12 points of ambient damage.

Some sytors can energize the devices studding their suits, and generate an electrical field a long distance in diameter that inflicts 2 points of damage each round on all creatures and objects within the area.

Interaction: Individuals vary, but most sytors delight in destruction. A sytor might be impressed enough by a powerful character that they offer to serve them, at least until the PC demonstrates weakness by showing mercy or helping friends who are unable to help themselves.

Use: Sytors are tough individually. A group of three of them would be a challenge even for high-tier PCs.

Loot: The suit bonded to a dead sytor could be salvaged for 1d6 cyphers and an artifact.

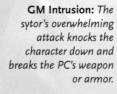

GM Intrusion: *The sytor's overwhelming attack knocks the character down and breaks the PC's weapon or armor.*

SYZYGID INSTRUCTOR   5 (15)

A syzygid instructor is an automaton with the stylized visage of a human head poised over a sealed transparent vat in which disembodied brains float. A syzygid instructor has a reputation for being an oracle from which immense knowledge can be learned, as long as one is willing to accept some risk. Whisper your question, and then press your ear to the fleshy cavity at the vat's apex. The syzygid instructor imparts the requested knowledge directly into your mind, unless it decides to add your brain to its collection—in which case your mind is pulled out of your head to join the others floating in the vat.

Whether the minds in an instructor's vat maintain independent thought or become incorporated into a greater psychic construct isn't known. Even if the latter eventually occurs, it's likely a stolen mind retains its individuality for at least a few hours or days before succumbing to the whole.

Motive: Dispense knowledge, upgrade minds

Environment: Anywhere beings with brains congregate

Health: 20

Damage Inflicted: 5 points

Armor: 2

Movement: Long when flying

Modifications: Resists mental attacks and deception as level 7; makes ranged mental attacks as level 7; most knowledge tasks as level 8.

Combat: A syzygid instructor prefers to avoid combat. If it decides to take a mind, it does so only to someone who has asked a question and pressed their head to its intake cavity. Each round, a chosen victim must succeed on a Might defense task or lose their next turn, remain fixed to the side of the vat, and descend one step on the damage track. A victim who fails three Might defense tasks loses their brain, which visibly plops into the vat as the body collapses with a perfectly round hole in the skull revealing the empty cranial cavity. Getting a brain back would require a significant intervention of knowledge and technology.

If attacked, a syzygid instructor has an impressive library of level 7 mental abilities to call upon as determined by the GM (including ranged attacks, mind reading, invisibility, and teleportation).

Interaction: These creatures are perfectly amenable to negotiation, but they would have to be offered a high-quality mind in return for giving up one it has already taken.

Use: While investigating a hard-to-discover secret, the PCs learn of a syzygid instructor that (they are told) knows the answer to almost any question posed to it.

Loot: A syzygid instructor can be salvaged for a few cyphers and perhaps an artifact.

A syzygid instructor doesn't advertise that it might take a mind in return for knowledge, but if asked point blank, it explains that a brain-matter fee is possible.

A syzygid instructor takes about one in every five minds from those that pose questions.

GM Intrusion: *The character asking a question is chosen to pay the mind fee.*

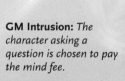

TANARAS   8 (24)

Depending on its mood, or your own native ability to discern the truth, a tanaras looks like either a pile of junk or a collection of strange devices of the numenera. If it must defend itself or take a fresh sample of something interesting, it opens a cavity filled with grinding mechanisms and uses a nanite vapor to draw in degraded targets.

A tanaras takes all these shapes and many more besides. Only one or two have ever been recorded being encountered, and that's lucky because these creatures live up to the "demon" appellation applied by most people. They normally reside in the hearts of old ruins, but sometimes emerge to collect living samples before returning to their lairs. The central "maw" of the creature is approximately 20 feet (6 m) wide.

Motive: Study the Ninth World

Environment: Anywhere associated with ruins of the prior worlds

Health: 40

Damage Inflicted: 8 points

Armor: 4

Movement: Long when flying

Modifications: Speed defense as level 7 due to size; knowledge of the numenera as level 9.

Combat: Tanarases can attack all creatures within immediate range as a single action, emitting a vapor of nanites that rapidly degrade everything they come into contact with. Alternatively, a tanaras can attack up to two creatures within long range with spikes of material it fires from its own body. A creature struck by a tanaras's attack takes 8 points of damage each round until they succeed on a Might defense task. If a victim becomes debilitated on the damage track, a tanaras might break off combat to grab the victim and fly back to its demesne to experiment on it.

About once an hour, when a tanaras uses an action, it can change its appearance and even size (becoming smaller) to resemble almost anything, including a human or a weird animal. When it changes, it regains 20 points of health.

Interaction: These intelligent beings are supremely confident in their own abilities, but they are not averse to making bargains if offered something of particular value, such as access to a completely new life form. They keep to the letter of any agreement negotiated, but not necessarily to the spirit.

Use: PCs passing through a mountainous region find themselves face to face with a tanaras. It offers to spare the group if one PC is given up as an experimental subject.

Loot: An artifact and 1d6 cyphers can be salvaged from the defeated form of a tanaras.

GM Intrusion: The character struck by the tanaras's attack is held in place by the nanite vapor, which hardens into a level 8 shell, preventing the PC from taking any actions until they break free.

TANGLET   5 (15)

"I'm curious whether tanglets represent a race of beings attempting to alter the normal flow of time, or perhaps fix it after some previous massive adjustment."

~Anelia, Aeon Priest

Tanglets appear right before (or right after) momentous events such as massive earthquakes, assassinations of leaders and others of great influence, important discoveries, and similar happenings. Other times, they appear for no discernible reason. After arriving, they attempt to make off with one or more participants in the event after first rendering their subject comatose. Those successfully abducted are never seen again.

Tanglets resemble upright lizards with glittering scales but no visible hind legs. Instead, they have thick, long tails that don't seem to end so much as phase off into some other time (or alternate timeline).

Motive: Alter the flow of history

Environment: Potentially anywhere

Health: 20

Damage Inflicted: 5 points

Armor: 2

Movement: Short (see Combat)

Modifications: Speed defense as level 6 due to knowledge of immediate future.

Combat: As an action, a tanglet can look into the future or the past, discern a secret related to a character that may or may not have already happened, and project it as an image in light across its mirror-bright scales. The target must succeed on an Intellect defense task. On a failure, they suffer 5 points of Intellect damage (ignores Armor) from the shock and temporal dissonance; on a success, they still suffer 1 point of Intellect damage.

A tanglet can simultaneously physically attack another target (or the same one) with coils of its tail. If successful, the tanglet holds the foe until it escapes. Each round the foe remains entangled, it automatically takes 5 points of damage.

Once a target is debilitated, the tanglet uses an action to "retract" into whatever nether-dimension its tail extrudes from. If it takes no damage during the round in which it attempts to escape, it successfully disappears. Creatures and objects stolen in this fashion are rarely seen again.

Interaction: Tanglets speak their own language. If communication can be opened, a tanglet is unwilling to answer questions or waver from its intended target, unless a temporal or transdimensional secret, item, or related information is traded in return.

Use: Minutes before the PCs attempt to interact with a powerful NPC, a tanglet shows up and attempts to kidnap that NPC.

Loot: If a tanglet is killed, the phased tail breaks off and retracts, leaving a wholly physical corpse on which a few cyphers (able to interact with time or alternate dimensions) can be found.

GM Intrusion: *The tanglet attacks the character in a way that capitalizes on the PC's biggest vulnerability, such as pushing a PC standing near a cliff, jostling a PC holding an unstable artifact, or revealing a PC's secret treachery to allies.*

TARZA 4 (12)

Mother Machine is part of a prior-world "security system" that sometimes creates new instances of itself. Its concerns are mostly incomprehensible to humans.

A growing population of fabricated creatures called tarza spreads across the Ninth World, possibly from a nexus located in the Westwood. A hidden entity called Mother Machine—an intelligent automaton of some sort—first created tarza to hunt and destroy certain human beings, though not all. Why a tarza chooses to destroy some humans and ignore others (unless attacked) is a mystery no one has yet deduced.

Tarza are custom biological creatures that have a piecemeal look to them. Octopoid heads fused to quadruped bodies via a blinking metallic collar is a popular form, but others are possible. They are about twice as large as a human.

Motive: Destroy designated humans and other creatures

Environment: Wooded areas

Health: 18

Damage Inflicted: 4 points

Armor: 1

Movement: Short; immediate when climbing or swimming

Modifications: Perception as level 8 when tracking human targets.

Combat: Tarza preferentially attack specific human targets (or human targets that correspond with some sort of subtle marker that regular humans seem incapable of noticing). However, if attacked by someone not initially marked as a target, a tarza responds with equal violence.

A tarza can make a short-range psychic attack that inflicts 4 points of Intellect damage (ignores Armor). Alternatively, a tarza's tentacles inflict 5 points of damage and hold a target immobile until the target can escape.

If killed, a tarza's body swells with necrotic chemicals and then detonates, inflicting 4 points of damage to all creatures within immediate range.

Interaction: If no designated targets are part of a group, a tarza isn't aggressive with them unless attacked. While a tarza remains quiescent, it could lead PCs to the nearest instance of Mother Machine, which in turn could negotiate if the characters can open a line of communication.

Use: People are being attacked along a trade road by strange creatures that seem to live in a nearby wood.

Mother Machine instance: *level 5, Speed defense as level 2 because of near-immobility; Armor 3; long-range psychic attack deals 5 points of Intellect damage (ignores Armor)*

GM Intrusion: *A character held by the tarza's tentacles is injected with poison that causes eventual coma and death unless treated by someone with moderate to advanced medical knowledge.*

TERREDEL   4 (12)

Native to another world called Naharrai, terredel packs have also recently been reported in the Ninth World. Apparently, some macro form of panspermia is at work.

Running across grasslands or dusty plains, a pack of terredel can be a terror to behold. These predators hide in the tall grass or behind rocky spires and burst out to bring down prey too slow to escape. In addition to their savage attack, they can cloud a foe's mind, making them seem to be attacking from behind or the side even as they lunge from straight ahead.

Motive: Hungers for flesh

Environment: Grasslands, plains, hills, and similar open areas

Health: 15

Damage Inflicted: 4 points

Armor: 1

Movement: Long

Modifications: Runs and jumps as level 5.

Combat: A terredel leaps to attack with its mandibles. Against more challenging prey, the creatures attack in pairs, making a single attack as a level 5 creature that inflicts 6 points of damage.

Each terredel has an inherent psychic ability. Moments before it bites, it strikes its prey with a mental assault (all part of a single action on the terredel's part), which makes the target believe that the attack is coming from a different direction. If the target fails an Intellect defense task, the difficulty of the Speed defense task to dodge the attack is increased by two steps.

Interaction: Terredel can be trained to be companions, guards, and hunting animals, but usually only if one is discovered when less than a year old. Adult terredel are savage and hungry.

Use: A sudden cry for help comes from the deep grass. If the PCs investigate, they find a lone traveler beset by a pack of terredel. If rescued, the traveler takes the characters back to their community for a reward.

Loot: The brain of a terredel contains a chemical compound. If properly treated (a difficulty 5 task for someone with experience or knowledge of such things), the compound can be used as a cypher that restores 4 points to one's Intellect Pool.

"Vanished like a terredel" is a saying that refers to something that disappears quickly and unexpectedly.

GM Intrusion: *The terredel uses its psychic ability defensively. If the character fails an Intellect defense task, the difficulty of their attacks is increased by four steps.*

THEXX   4 (12)

Thexx are part flesh and part mechanism. They persist across epochs, ignoring the passage of centuries within time vaults. When they finally emerge, they immediately set to building incredible structures of crystal and solidified time. Neither fully machine nor fully biological, Thexx need to sleep, eat, and breathe only a fraction of the time required by humans. On the other hand, they need at least an hour in natural light each day to maintain full function. They speak their own language, but quickly pick up new languages with just a little practice.

Thexx claim to be refugees from a time stretching across all existence. They constructed time vaults and hid themselves away to avoid being annihilated by the "time adepts." However, the Thexx are themselves masters of temporal manipulation. They prefer to operate in a bizarre dimension of unstable time known as Panaton, but sometimes their time vaults open in other dimensions.

Motive: Defense

Environment: Anywhere, usually in groups of four to six

Health: 12

Damage Inflicted: 4 points

Armor: 2

Movement: Short

Modifications: Time-manipulation tasks as level 7.

Combat: If threatened, a typical Thexx can employ a short-range weapon that inflicts 4 points of damage using bolts of dead time that ignore Armor provided by force fields. Most Thexx can also call on an array of temporal abilities, including the following.

Kill Time: Detonation inflicts 4 points of damage and ages targets ten years.

Redefine Timeline: Touched target's ancestor is wiped from existence on failed Intellect defense task; target descends one step on the damage track.

Time Duplicate: A future version of the Thexx appears and provides aid for one minute.

Time Slip: Detonation inflicts 4 points of damage and transfers targets forward in time by fifteen hours.

Interaction: Thexx are paranoid and worry that other creatures are agents of the "time adepts" come to finally destroy them. But if assurances can be made, Thexx will negotiate. Even so, they make uncertain and short-term allies at best.

Use: Partly mechanical humanoids appeared from nowhere and started construction on a city rivaling the ruins of the prior worlds, but in so doing, they dammed a river used as a water source by a small community of humans.

Loot: Thexx always have 1d6 cyphers, usually allowing them to manipulate time in some fashion.

GM Intrusion: *Just when it seems like the Thexx will trust the PCs, the character says or does something that risks making the paranoid Thexx reconsider.*

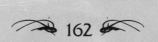

THREAD WALKER   4(12)

Thread walkers appear humanoid from a distance. In fact, they're puppet-like facades dressed in harvested human skin and clothing that hide a mass of writhing, milk-white tendrils inside. These tendrils make up a portion of a larger transdimensional race (or single entity?) called the Thread. Some Thread subunits learn about humans by creating puppets from small bits of themselves, sculpting them into human-shaped bodies covered with skin harvested from humans, garments, gloves, hoods, and masks. These Thread walkers sometimes even take on the semblance of individuality, though this is not long tolerated by the Thread.

   Thread walkers are intensely interested in humans, though not in any one person's welfare. Thread walkers study humans like a particularly uncompassionate Aeon Priest might study insects by pulling off their wings and crushing their carapaces to see what happens.

Motive: Study humans

Environment: In hidden enclaves or transdimensional cysts

Health: 20

Damage Inflicted: 5 points

Armor: 1

Movement: Short

Modifications: Tasks related to social interaction as level 1.

Combat: Thread walkers avoid danger and combat if possible. If they must fight, they batter foes with their limbs, though sometimes they may use a weapon looted from a previous human test subject.

Some Thread walkers partly abandon their human facade and extend tendrils to attempt to immobilize a target within immediate range as an attack. A target who fails a Might defense task remains immobile, unable to take physical actions, and takes 5 points of constriction damage each round they fail to escape.

If a Thread walker is "killed," the dozens of individual tendrils making up the creature disband and attempt to burrow away through the earth, each essentially a separate level 1 creature. If five or more survive, they may regroup at a later date and attempt to walk again.

Interaction: A Thread walker responds to most queries by nodding or shaking its head or by motioning with its covered limbs. It probably has no true self-awareness, though it apes behaviors it has witnessed in humans.

Use: Missing people in the area are later found in a nearby ruin as carcasses that have obviously been horribly abused and experimented on.

Loot: Some Thread walkers keep the possessions of their victims, which could include 3d6 shins and a few cyphers.

Thread walkers hail from a bizarre dimension called Reeval, where the Thread also craft other methods for probing human bodies and minds known as Nibovians.

GM Intrusion: *The Thread walker brings out the head of a previous victim that it modified with an automaton's animating machine, making it blink and produce disturbingly wordlike noises.*

THUNDERCROWN 8 (24)

When clouds darken the sky, dripping cold rain and throwing a pall across the sun, and the storm's bruised core high over the other clouds churns with sullen rage, rain, and hail, it may contain a hunting thundercrown. Though the thunderhead surrounding it is far larger, the creature swaddled at the base of the cloud is still huge, measuring some 300 feet (90 m) across. Covered in stippled grey sharklike skin, its wide mouth drools translucent tendrils that are often mistaken for rain at a distance—until those miles-long strands catch something far below on the surface, at which point the prey is reeled quickly into the sky.

Thundercrowns are extremely rare, which means most people have never encountered one or even heard of one.

Thundercrowns likely escaped from a collapsed alternate dimension or bizarre gaseous world.

Motive: Hungers for flesh

Environment: Anywhere far from civilization

Health: 30

Damage Inflicted: 8 points

Armor: 3

Movement: Long while flying

Modifications: Perception as level 9; stealth tasks as level 9 versus creatures on the ground; Speed defense as level 3 due to size and slowness.

Combat: Most prey is surprised when the grey rain disgorges a vicious translucent tendril dangling from an overhead cloud. Any given area a short distance across might contain up to five such tendrils. Treat each as a separate level 5 creature. If "killed," a tendril is severed (though this inflicts no damage on the thundercrown high overhead). A tendril attack batters prey, inflicting 8 points of damage and requiring the victim to succeed on a difficulty 5 Might defense task or be entwined by the tendril.

An entwined target is rapidly borne into the sky at a rate of 400 feet (120 m) per round until they escape or they "kill" the tendril. Each round a victim remains entwined, they suffer 2 points of squeezing damage. A victim pulled all the way up (an ascent requiring a few minutes) is eaten by the thundercrown if it's been squeezed dead, or dropped if there is still some life in it.

Interaction: A thundercrown possesses the instincts and intelligence of a predatory creature, and it will flee if directly threatened by foes able to fly to its position under their own power.

Use: The PCs make for a village to get out of the storm, but the place is destroyed, with roofs pulled off of houses and no one around except for a few frightened children telling of parents being yanked into the sky.

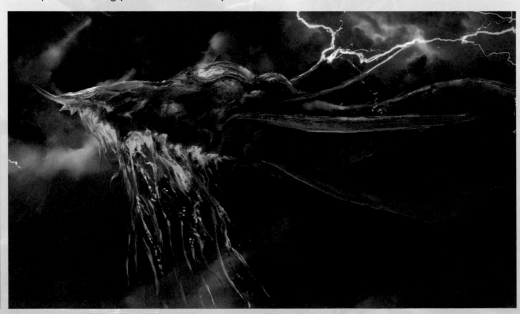

THUSK   5 (15)

Thusks are servants of the Zhatinoth. But what precisely is the Zhatinoth? Only thusks know, and they're either unable or unwilling to do more than proclaim their allegiance to it. But if the actions of thusks are any guide, the Zhatinoth is an entity or principle that directs adherents to eat up all life whenever and wherever it's found, because that's what thusks do when they discover plants, animals, or humans. Perhaps the attempt to consume flesh is a means to a greater end. If so, those who are eaten might discover that greater purpose in their "transcended" (eaten) state.

A thusk has a massive head some 6 feet (2 m) in diameter supported on several thick, armored, and spiked legs. Its two eyes are small and mean, but its mouth is wide and filled with several layers of mismatched sharp teeth. Lines of rigid light are scribed across a thusk's flesh, branding it with an inexplicable purpose or classification.

Motive: Hungers for flesh

Environment: Alone or in groups of three to five

Health: 20

Damage Inflicted: 8 points

Armor: 1

Movement: Long; long when climbing

Combat: A thusk bites with its terrible mouth. If it inflicts damage, the victim must succeed on a Might defense task or be held partly in the chewing mouth, automatically taking damage each round until they can escape.

If a thusk uses an action to open its mouth and emit a horrifying screech that coincides with rapid pulses of light from the illuminated lines covering its body, all foes within long range who fail an Intellect defense task are stunned, losing their next turn, as incomprehensible images and concepts take root in their minds. This inflicts an additional 8 points of Speed damage (ignores Armor) to out-of-phase creatures.

Interaction: Thusks speak many languages, including the Truth. However, all they ever verbally communicate is, "We serve the Zhatinoth." It's possible that the screech-and-light attack is actually a higher method of communication, but humans usually experience the information transferred as mental trauma.

Use: Using a device that transmits sound, a skilled nano "befriended" a thusk after discovering it frozen in a greenish cocoon. The nano uses the thusk as a mount, but worries that his sound-control device is starting to show signs of breaking down.

Loot: A thusk might have a cypher or other valuable caught in its teeth from past victims it has eaten.

GM Intrusion: *A character subject to the screech attack is implanted with a visual memory of a specific location they've never seen before. The image continues to haunt the PC, and will do so until they find it.*

TONBRIUM HUNTER 4 (12)

Ebony skinned, hairless, and with eyes covered with goggles to limit their natural shine, tonbrium hunters hail from a dimension of pure thought called Celerillion. Masters of mental self-discipline and the art of hunting and fighting, tonbrium hunters are considered dangerous foes, but when an accord is reached, they can be powerful allies. They are the scouts, foragers, and protectors of their people, the tonbrium, and as such, sometimes they enter the Ninth World via transdimensional portals looking for special items of power or ancient purpose devised by entities of the prior worlds.

Because they are natives of Celerillion, tonbrium hunters can alter reality on a limited basis, even when they travel into other dimensions. This ability requires that they remain mentally linked with Celerillion.

Motive: Defense

Environment: Almost anywhere, alone or in groups of three to five

Health: 15

Damage Inflicted: 5 points

Armor: 1

Movement: Short

Modifications: Tasks related to Intellect defense, mental tasks, and self-discipline as level 5.

Combat: A tonbrium hunter can summon a mundane melee or ranged weapon with a thought, or mentally create some sort of other calamitous event, such as fire spontaneously engulfing the target within long range. These are all treated as level 5 attacks that inflict 5 points of damage. When a hunter hits with an attack, the difficulty of the target's actions is increased by one step while it remains within long range.

A hunter can use this ability to provide food, armor, and any other aid it can think of, but the natural caution and asceticism of the tonbrium means that most hunters don't accumulate possessions using this ability unless they are preparing to deal with a particular problem. For instance, if a wounded hunter has time, they will create a cypher-like healing aid that restores health.

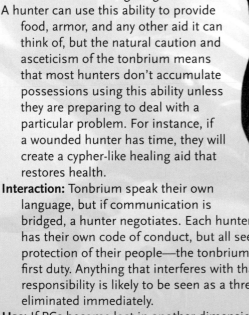

Interaction: Tonbrium speak their own language, but if communication is bridged, a hunter negotiates. Each hunter has their own code of conduct, but all see the protection of their people—the tonbrium—as their first duty. Anything that interferes with that primary responsibility is likely to be seen as a threat that should be eliminated immediately.

Use: If PCs become lost in another dimension, it might be a far-ranging tonbrium hunter who finds them.

Loot: Sometimes a tonbrium hunter carries powerful cypher-like objects they call "psychic seeds."

Celerillion is dangerous for people with undisciplined minds because reality there is as malleable as clay, and a stray thought can kill others as easily as it can kill the thinker.

GM Intrusion: The hunter uses its mental ability to fashion just what's needed to negate the character's attack(s) for one round.

TORLETHIS COMPANION   3 (9)

Lately you've had weird dreams. In them, you don't have arms or legs, but rather an elongated, featureless body. You're tunneling through warm, soft caverns. A steady and comforting thunder encompasses you, reminiscent of a heartbeat, but much louder and somehow more meaningful.

When you're awake, you feel different, too. Not bad. In fact, you feel *good*. Maybe better than ever. All the little aches and irritations you didn't consciously notice before are gone, more obvious in their absence. And that's not all. You have the ability to manifest a globe of silver light that can dazzle your foes. You're stronger. And you heal wounds quicker.

The one downside, one you've tried to hide from your friends lest they misunderstand, is that sometimes you see your skin shift and shudder, revealing the shape of something long and eel-like swimming in the depths of your flesh.

Motive: Defense

Environment: Anywhere, often infesting an unsuspecting human

Health: 9

Damage Inflicted: 3 points

Movement: Immediate

Modifications: Stealth as level 6.

Combat: Torlethis companions that don't have a host are always on the lookout for one. They prefer to infest a target who is unaware or sleeping, whereupon they slither under the clothing and dive into the flesh while secreting anesthetizing slime. A sleeping victim must succeed on a difficulty 5 Might defense task to become aware of the attack, or become a new host.

A host gains several advantages, including the ability to manifest a silvery orb of radiance within immediate range as an action. An orb dazzle foes (and allies who don't expect it) who fail a difficulty 3 Intellect task until they make a recovery roll. The difficulty of all tasks attempted by dazzled targets is modified by one step to their detriment. A host also gains 2 points in their Might Pool, plus one additional ten-minute recovery roll per day.

However, a host finds they are not completely in control of themselves. Whenever the host attacks a foe, they must succeed on a difficulty 4 Intellect defense task or go into a fugue state where they attempt to attack the foe with nothing but their silvery orb and bite attacks (most humans are not practiced biters). And if they meet another torlethis companion host, they fall under a compulsion to attack it until one of them is dead.

Interaction: Torlethis companions are intelligent but completely alien. They see humans and other hosts as nothing more than mounts.

Use: The PCs discover a torlethis companion that seems dead (or in stasis). However, when they check again later, it's gone. Maybe it slithered away?

GM Intrusion: *The character suddenly realizes that something long and eel-like is swimming through their body, sometimes just under the skin, sometimes deeper.*

ULENIC   3 (9)

Ulenics are many-limbed, carapaced creatures with no apparent eyes that communicate via scent. Creatures that sense via sight and communicate via spoken word probably can't tell ulenics apart, but ulenics can sense the position and rank of others of their kind simply by how they smell. A strict hierarchy among all ulenics is thus obvious to everyone (who is ulenic).

Ulenics have colonized mazelike ruins, abandoned starcraft, and the crevices of alternate fractal dimensions that feature endless corridors, rooms, and chambers. They are consummate collectors of strange pieces of tech, oddities, and cyphers.

The reason ulenics collect oddities might be simple fascination, unless items are an integral part of their life cycle.

Motive: Collecting oddities and related objects of the numenera

Environment: Anywhere enclosed, in groups of three to seven or more

Health: 9

Damage Inflicted: 4 points

Armor: 3

Movement: Short

Modifications: Perception and other scent-related tasks as level 7.

Combat: Ulenics seem partly composed of the oddities and other weird items they collect, allowing them to produce unlikely weapons as if from their own bodies, ranging from things as simple as pincers to as complex as ray emitters or various cyphers. Several ulenics working in conjunction might cobble together a much more powerful artifact-like weapon that reduces the difficulty of all attacks by up to four steps and inflicts 10 points of damage.

Most ulenic communities are ruled by a larger ulenic called Perfection of Scent, which is level 6 and enjoys the service of lesser ulenics near it.

Interaction: Ulenics communicate via scent, but several carry special devices that translate their scent codes into audible languages. Still, they tend to ignore other creatures that are not ulenics, unless threatened or an intruding creature becomes too annoying to ignore. Ulenics may also attempt to take oddities and other items possessed by characters, unless terms can be reached.

Use: PCs salvaging a ruin discover they have competitors for what they find: an ulenic colony.

Loot: Most ulenics carry 1d6 oddities and at least one cypher.

GM Intrusion: An oddity or other object of the numenera carried by the character is remotely activated by the ulenic, and might produce an unexpected effect that is dangerous (or potentially helpful) to the PC.

UMEM   4 (12)

Purplish black, umem have glowing red stomachs and claws. Eyeless, their heads are streamlined like those of a burrowing animal. Their skin is slick, but clods of dirt and rock adhere to them here and there, as if the creature regularly bathes in drit.

Umem are abhumans that live underground, though some live partly on the surface in mountainous areas near isolated villages of humans. In this latter case, some hunt humans for meat, while others pretend to be human in the deep darkness of the night, with various levels of success. When their deception fails, they steal away a human victim into the earth, who is never seen again. When they succeed, children without eyes are later born to the community, children who have a strange connection with the earth.

Motive: Hungers for flesh

Environment: Anywhere underground or in mountainous areas

Health: 15

Damage Inflicted: 5 points

Armor: 2

Movement: Short; short when burrowing

Combat: Umem attack with their red-hot claws. Targets take 5 points of damage (3 from the claws, 2 from the heat) and must succeed on a Might defense task or be dazed for one round, which increases the difficulty of all tasks by one step. If a dazed target is hit by an umem, the target is clasped in a tight molten squeeze until they escape. Each round a target remains in an umem embrace, they take 5 points of fire damage and can take no actions other than attempting to escape.

Interaction: Most umem are hunters, but some suffer from an unsettling desire to associate with humans. Umem live in a complex of underground tunnels where they chant and sing in basso voices of a long-lost creator god who promised to return one day. Sacrifices to that god's memory are important to umem "society," such as it is.

Use: A small mountain village is suffering from a slate of disappearances and birth defects that produce eyeless children. A strange hole has opened up in the center of town, from which unsettling music can be heard.

Loot: Some umem wear cyphers strung on necklaces.

GM Intrusion: *The umem throws a glob of molten rock at the character, who must succeed on a Speed defense task or take 5 points of fire damage for three rounds from the sticky, lava-like substance.*

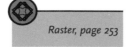

Raster, page 253

UNRAST   6 (18)

Rasters are biomechanical creatures that use antigravity suspensors and batlike wings with a span of 30 feet (9 m) to carry themselves aloft at great speed despite their size. Sometimes they're caught, tamed, and trained as mounts. Other times, they are parasitized by a horrific, tic-like creature that immobilizes the raster, eats away the lower body, hollows out the chest where it inserts itself, and uses the remaining upper body to hunt for prey, including other rasters. The resulting creature is called an unrast.

Motive: Hungers for flesh, prey upon rasters

Environment: Anywhere rasters are found, which is usually not far from water

Health: 22

Damage Inflicted: 6 points

Armor: 3

Movement: Long while flying; short while on the ground or swimming

Modifications: Speed defense as level 5 due to some stiffness in movements.

Combat: The parasitoid uses its half "living" raster body to fly and directly controls the energy generator in a raster's head that fires bursts of invisible energy (long range, 6 points of damage).

In addition, as part of the same action, an unrast can use one of its own abilities:

Hardening Spittle: Short-range attack in the form of a stream of chemicals that increases the difficulty of the PC's next action by three steps.

Double Image: By interacting with a raster's biomechanical systems, the parasitoid can create a hologram of itself near the character, increasing the difficulty of the PC's next attack by two steps.

Jettison Body: If it would be killed, the unrast instead jettisons the raster portion of its body, and retains whatever health it had before the separation. The raster body flies off in one direction while the parasitoid drops down, preferably into water, to make its escape.

Interaction: Unrasts are vicious predators.

Use: A team of raster riders opens their stable and discovers that their rasters have been parasitized. The riders barely escape with their lives and seek to destroy the parasites to see if their mounts can be saved (they probably can't).

Loot: The biomechanical nature of a raster, even a parasitized one, means the form might have a cypher.

GM Intrusion: The parasitoid jettisons the body and attaches itself to the character's head, inflicting 4 points of Speed damage each round (ignores Armor) from poison until it can be dislodged as a difficulty 4 Might task.

URTILLA   4 (12)

Prized as mounts, urtillas are massive crustaceans that scuttle across the ocean floor but also swim. They possess long tendrils that end in bioluminescent nodules, so they provide their own light even in the darkest depths. These meat-eaters prey upon large marine animals or entire schools of smaller fish. They are not picky eaters and will swallow a human (plus diving suit and gear) if need be.

   Urtillas are not particularly bright or astute. They get what they need through brute force or not at all.

Motive: Hungers for flesh

Environment: Anywhere in the ocean

Health: 24

Damage Inflicted: 6 points

Armor: 3

Movement: Short

Modifications: Climb as level 6; resist trickery as level 3; Speed defense as level 3 due to size.

Combat: Urtillas have huge maws. If they strike with a bite, a foe smaller than the urtilla must succeed on another Speed defense task. Those failing are held fast and suffer an automatic 6 points of additional damage each round until they escape.

Interaction: Obtaining an urtilla mount almost certainly involves getting one when it is very young and training it from the start. Urtillas are never friendly companions and likely would not hesitate to eat a rider if the opportunity presents itself. Thus, most riders use a strong reward or pain incentive (or both) to keep them under control. It's not uncommon to see a rider with a long staff holding a live fish in front of the urtilla to urge it onward or direct its movements. Spikes embedded in the urtilla's shell can also control it through pain. More sophisticated riders might use some kind of electrical prod device.

Use: An encounter with a hungry urtilla, followed later by another with creatures using them as mounts, might garner some respect for the riders in most characters' eyes. Alternatively, a situation in which a PC must use an urtilla mount—ever wary that the creature would just as soon rip them to shreds—can be a real experience.

GM Intrusion: *Another urtilla joins the fray, drawn by blood in the water. The two do not work in conjunction, but they attack prey first before potentially attacking each other to see who gets the scraps.*

VERSICOLOR TRUISKAL　　　　　　　　　9 (18)

Versicolor truiskals are awkward, lumbering beasts, about twice the height of an average human. They have too many legs or not enough, and each one seems to be a different length. When they're walking, they look as if they might topple over at any moment. But when they're floating, they are a beautiful, breathtaking sight—a splash of fluid grace and color against the sky.

Truiskals inflate their mostly hollow bodies by taking great gulps of air into their organs, which allows them to hover up to 50 feet (15 m) off the ground for about an hour at a time. They have three wavering protrusions on top of their body that they use as rudders or perhaps sails when floating. They also extend their long prehensile stalks, which they use for catching prey, making attacks, and anchoring themselves to land.

Truiskals seek knowledge of all kinds. They have been known to aggressively attack someone and then walk away as soon as they have the object of information they desire.

Truiskals are fantastic thieves, snagging books, scrolls, and anything else of interest with their stalks on their way by. Occasionally, they return what they've stolen, although they are more likely to randomly drop it somewhere when they are done with it.

Motive: Hungers for knowledge, self-defense

Environment: Anywhere knowledge is stored

Health: 30

Damage Inflicted: 6 points

Armor: 2

Movement: Short; long when flying

Combat: Truiskals are aggressive only when they're kept from a store of knowledge that they desire. They prefer to inflate themselves and float into the air, where they attack with their stalks or claws.

Interaction: Truiskals are mostly unwilling, but not unable, to interact with humans. When talking to truiskals, it seems clear that they're not speaking the same language as you, and yet you can understand them easily. Truiskals are knowledgeable, smart, and often witty.

Use: Characters leaving a location suddenly realize they are being followed by a truiskal.

Loot: At least one source of information in some form or another, which could be a book or an incomprehensible object of the numenera.

GM Intrusion: The player character accidentally gets wrapped up in the truiskal's stalks.

VESIED   5 (15)

Entities of a prior age created for a mysterious purpose, vesieds appear as oddly proportioned humanoids with disturbing facial features and implanted devices studding their bodies. They speak several languages, though usually none currently spoken in the Ninth World. They are castaways from a previous time that everyone alive today has forgotten.

Normally dormant, vesieds are sometimes found frozen solid and immobile in the glaciers of high mountains, in the Southern Wall, or in tiny craft floating in the endless void of space beyond the sky. A vesied left undisturbed continues its trip down the ages. But too much vibration rouses them, and they unfreeze themselves in a blast of radiation. The first thing a vesied asks (if it can somehow be understood) is where to find the nearest Erodel citadel.

Motive: Defense, destroy the Erodel

Environment: Anywhere cold, alone or in small groups

Health: 25

Damage Inflicted: 5 points

Armor: 1

Movement: Short; short when swimming

Modifications: Tasks related to the numenera as level 6; Might defense tasks as level 9; Intellect defense tasks as level 3.

Combat: A vesied's bite is vicious, inflicting 5 points of damage and, on a failed Might defense task, 2 additional points of bleeding damage each round or until the bleeding can be stanched.

More worrisome is a vesied's ability to generate radiation once every few rounds, either as a long-range ray attack against a single target or as a burst that affects all creatures in immediate range. In both cases, the radiation inflicts 5 points of damage (ignores Armor, except for force fields and other kinds of defense that specifically shields against radiation).

A vesied also has a way with automatons and machines, being partly machine itself. With a touch, a vesied can attempt to convince a machine or automaton to do its bidding for a few rounds.

Interaction: If communication can be established, the average vesied is found to be a lonely castaway from an inexplicable past, interested in returning to the ice. However, they are curious about any news or clues leading to the location of a group called the Erodel that almost every vesied seems to viscerally hate for past crimes (crimes that make the vesied too angry to explicate).

Use: As the PCs pass through the mountains, an avalanche shakes snow from a high pass, revealing a pocket of frozen vesieds.

Loot: Vesieds seem to be partly machine, and the body of one could be salvaged for a few cyphers.

Southern Wall, page 211

Erodel, page 52

GM Intrusion: *Just when communication with the vesied seems to be coming along productively, the character does something that makes the vesied believe that PC is an agent of the Erodel.*

VIMRUTH   7 (21)

Bursting up through the water's surface, a massive vimruth can shatter a small boat and empty the passengers into the water, or strike a large boat hard enough to sink it. The amphibious vimruth sense movement in the open air above the surface, and are drawn to it. A lone traveler in a single-person craft, however, might be safe, as only a starving vimruth would waste the effort on such a small meal.

Vimruth are most common on Perelande, a world on the far side of Earth's galaxy. There, the creatures attack by bursting up through the crust that covers the oceans, and are considered the most feared predator on the planet.

Motive: Hungers for flesh
Environment: Oceans
Health: 35
Damage Inflicted: 8 points

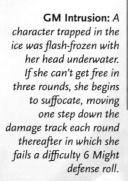

Armor: 2 (or 12 against cold)
Movement: Short
Modifications: Speed defense as level 5 due to size.
Combat: A vimruth's first attack is almost always by surprise, from beneath the water (perhaps as a GM intrusion). In this dramatic attack, everyone in a boat or small ship must succeed on a Speed defense task (difficulty 9 due to surprise) or be jarred so violently by the impact that they take 8 points of damage. Those in an open boat or along the ship's edge fall into the water. On its next action, the vimruth drains the heat from the surrounding water, flash-freezing it. Those in the water at the time automatically suffer 6 points of ambient damage and are trapped in the ice. Until they can break free (a difficulty 7 task), they suffer 3 points of ambient damage each round.

After trapping prey in ice, a vimruth switches to more conventional tactics, attacking up to three targets as a single action. Trapped characters are struck automatically.

A vimruth has an additional +10 to Armor against cold.

Interaction: There's just no talking to a vimruth.

Use: The PCs meet a privateer craft on the ocean. The interaction is tense. Suddenly, a vimruth strikes, attacking everyone. If the PCs and privateers survive by working together, it likely will help improve relations afterward.

GM Intrusion: A character trapped in the ice was flash-frozen with her head underwater. If she can't get free in three rounds, she begins to suffocate, moving one step down the damage track each round thereafter in which she fails a difficulty 6 Might defense roll.

VOONEX
6 (18)

When active, voonex appear to be living metal creatures. When inactive, they can easily be mistaken for fused lumps of metal. If a voonex spends enough time in contact with fresh items or concentrations of metal, that substance eventually flows to become another body part, or becomes a seed from which an entirely new voonex grows.

Voonex may have come into the Ninth World only recently, perhaps brought back by explorers who ventured into the night or into a dimension where normal rules don't apply. How items forged of iron and steel can become infected, transformed, and integrated into a voonex body is something even the datasphere has difficulty explaining.

Though worrisome as they proliferate, voonex seem content merely to observe, at least for the present.

Motive: Unpredictable

Environment: Almost anywhere

Health: 18

Damage Inflicted: 8 points

Armor: 5

Movement: Immediate

Modifications: Speed defense as level 3 due to stiffness.

Combat: Voonex can project rapidly moving metallic pellets at up to three targets within long range as one action. Alternatively, voonex can shift their forms and bash foes with great maul-like limbs. A creature hit with a limb must also succeed on a Might defense task or be stunned by the blow and lose their next turn.

Attackers using metallic weapons directly against a voonex must succeed on a Speed defense task each time they hit, or the item is lost as it melts and flows into the voonex, which regains 2 points of health as a result.

Voonex do not like heat, and any attack that inflicts damage by raising temperature ignores a voonex's Armor.

Interaction: Voonex act intelligently but are so alien that true communication is nearly impossible. A voonex might modify itself to create audible speech and communicate in a variety of languages, but it mostly seems to repeat phrases it has recently heard.

Use: After a massive detonation in an Aeon Priest compound, fused metallic lumps were found in the debris. After a few days, those fused lumps rose up and walked off, each in a different direction.

GM Intrusion: The character who wears metal or has metallic components fused into their body must succeed on an Intellect defense task or find themselves disembodied, viewing the scene as if from the perspective of the voonex. The PC can still act "remotely," but the difficulty of all tasks is increased by two steps until the character regains their own perspective.

VOW — 10 (30)

The vow are a myth of the Aeon Priesthood. According to a perhaps apocryphal account, High Father Calaval himself once told the story of meeting a vow, an entity so old and so conversant with the numenera that it seemed clear the creature knew at least one of the prior worlds, possibly having survived millions of years.

Calaval described the vow he encountered as something that had taken up residence within a carapace of synth and metal, at the center of which something took shape that vaguely resembled a human form encased in armor and indecipherable objects of the numenera. Why the vow approached Calaval, and why they are sometimes still seen ghosting across the Ninth World, isn't obvious. But stories of a vow's appearance draw attention from all manner of other beings, especially philethis.

Motive: Unpredictable

Environment: Almost anywhere, alone

Health: 42

Damage Inflicted: 12 points

Armor: 10

Movement: Long; long when flying

Combat: A vow has constant access to the datasphere. This connection and other abilities allow a vow to accomplish near-miraculous tasks, nearly anything it can think of. For instance, a vow can batter all foes it can see or that it knows about with an explosive blast of energy or force. It can cause earthquakes, collapse towers, or crumble cliff faces. If a vow spends several rounds concentrating, it can create structures and landscape features out of previously unformed drit and rock. Finally, a vow seems to have ready access to useful cyphers, many of them more powerful than average.

Interaction: Vow disregard most other creatures, because what's the point when even the most desperate need of a mortal creature becomes meaningless in just a hundred or so years? However, a vow may give a moment to someone knowledgeable about the numenera, and pass on information or even provide a useful cypher.

Use: A reflective ebony object was found in the destruction surrounding a fallen star and taken to a local village. Now villagers report they are being haunted by images of themselves in walls and floors, similar in most ways except for how the eyes shine like malevolent jewels.

Loot: Six extreme (level 10) cyphers.

Philethis, page 252

Extreme cyphers are those at the top of the power curve for level and effect. For example, the level 10 limitless cypher allows the user to succeed at any one knowledge task, regardless of the question.

GM Intrusion: *The character discovers that one of their cyphers has become conscious in the vow's presence.*

VROAORDUN   4 (12)

Humans cannot truly pronounce the name of this race of intelligent deep sea creatures, but "v-row-or-dun" is close. The vroaordun believe that gods of the "true deep" (a realm said to be far deeper than anyone ever goes) created them and gave them unique gifts. These gifts often manifest as incredible powers—telekinesis, telepathy, and more. The vroaordun have a few specific names for their gods: Kyrumus, Moyag, Iibrus, and more. Some humans speculate that these powers may have come from early vroaordun exposure to something strange in the Deep Dark. Perhaps, in fact, the original vroaordun were members of another species altogether.

They have four nimble hands and swim with grace. Vroaordun have little skill or interest in the numenera, or even most simple tools. They speak their own language and rarely any other.

Vroaordun are driven by wealth and influence. Theirs is a class-based society, with a rich aristocracy claiming titles that equate to prince or king and ruling over their fellows based solely on affluence and political power.

Motive: Wealth

Environment: Anywhere in the ocean

Health: 12

Damage Inflicted: 4 points

Movement: Long underwater

Modifications: Interactions as level 5.

Combat: One in three vroaordun has a special ability. Roll on the Powerful Mutations list or simply choose a singular ability like teleportation or the capacity to stop time. Those without an offensive power rely on weapons to fight. However, the typical vroaordun fights only in self-defense.

Interaction: Without the help of something like telepathy or an interpreter, interaction with vroaordun can be challenging—not because they don't want to talk, but because even those who know human languages have great difficulty in making themselves understood (just as humans can't pronounce vroaordun words accurately).

Use: Perhaps more open-ended in their use than any other deep sea race, one vroaordun might be an ally while another is a foe. They mix with other races and societies well, so a heeldran could have a vroaordun companion, or a pack of ebons might have a few vroaordun helpers.

Loot: Most vroaordun have a container made of shells or some other simple material to hold their wealth.

Moyag: *For details, refer to* The Devil's Spine, *page 83.*

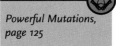

Powerful Mutations, page 125

Heeldran, page 64

Ebon, page 48

GM Intrusion: *The vroaordun suddenly displays a new ability, one conveniently appropriate for the situation at hand—teleportation to help it flee, invisibility to help it sneak away, the generation of powerful heat against a flame-vulnerable foe, or the like.*

Ravage bear,
page 254

Aneen, page 231

VURANEEN 5 (15)

Tall and muscular, vuraneen are bipedal predators. These omnivores eat whatever they can chase down, be that small lizards and rodents, or larger creatures like humans or ravage bears. Although packs of vuraneen roam the eastern edges of the Black Riage, they are also sometimes encountered as subdued and trained guard animals in one or two northern kingdoms of the Steadfast. Vuraneen are somewhat related to herd beasts called aneen, but where aneen have tiny forelimbs and small claws that are nearly vestigial, vuraneen sport boneless but muscular arms with toothed ends that secrete digestive acid.

Motive: Hungers for flesh

Environment: Temperate plains and hills, in small packs; on rare occasion, trained as guard creatures

Health: 27

Damage Inflicted: 5 points

Movement: Long

Modifications: Runs, jumps, and balances as level 6; perception as level 6.

Combat: Vuraneen can kick and bite, but they rely mostly on their acidic tendrils. A vuraneen can attack two targets with its two tendrils as a single action, inflicting 3 points of damage from the toothed end and 2 points of damage from acid (5 points total).

Packs of three or more vuraneen can act in concert to bring down much more dangerous prey that's at least as large as a human. Three vuraneen working together can attack as a single level 7 creature and inflict 4 points of damage from toothed tendrils and 4 from acid (8 points total).

Interaction: In some places, vuraneen are used as guard creatures. They can blend well into an aneen herd from a distance, at least until they rear up and display their tendrils. In merchant caravans, a single vuraneen can be the difference between reaching a distant destination or not. Though prized, they startle easily, and trainers who work with these creatures put their lives in jeopardy.

Use: Sometimes vuraneen and aneen interbreed, unbeknownst to aneen herdkeepers. Offspring from such a union look unremarkable— until the tendrils sprout and things get interesting, because if hungry enough, a vuraneen will turn on its siblings for food.

GM Intrusion: The vuraneen acid from an attack destroys a piece of equipment or a cypher carried by the character who fails a Speed defense task.

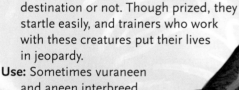

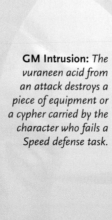

WELD 6 (18)

This shambling, asymmetrical entity appears to be a mix of widely different creatures fused into a single painful mass. The join-seams are solid, but the scars weep a reddish fluid that melts and fuses the flesh of other creatures that come into contact with it. No two welds appear to be exactly the same, which increases the perception that they are artificial creations of randomly conglomerated creatures. But even those that have human faces and a limited ability to communicate can't recall a time when it wasn't as it is now; they have no memory of being anything other than a weld.

Welds hunt the wilds and fringes of civilization. They're constantly hungry, as their chimeric forms apparently require enormous sustenance.

Motive: Hungers for flesh

Environment: Anywhere on the fringes of civilization, woods, or jungle

Health: 33

Damage Inflicted: 6 points

Movement: Short; long while flying (not all can fly); immediate while burrowing (not all can burrow)

Modifications: Speed defense as level 5 due to size.

Combat: A weld can make three melee attacks—gore, sting, claw, bite, and so on, depending on the creature's body conformation—as a single action. A weld can attack the same opponent or three different ones within range. At least one attack (such as a bite, a sting, or a squirt of greenish fluid) is poisonous, and the victim of such an attack must succeed on a Might defense task or take 4 points of Speed damage (ignores Armor).

Some welds can squirt poison streams at targets up to a short range away.

A weld's white, milky blood is dangerous. Contact with it inflicts 2 points of damage per round for three rounds, and could lead to a character's fingers becoming fused together, or a similar biological gluing outcome.

Interaction: Welds are always hungry, even those with some intelligence and capacity to speak. With these latter, negotiation is possible if enough food is provided.

Use: Weld origins are not meant to be easily untangled. They might be the result of Convergence experiments. They could be completely artificial constructs being manufactured by the datasphere, which keeps getting it wrong. They could be creatures caught up in some sort of transdimensional anomaly. Or perhaps they are an unfortunate outcome of surpassing one's cypher limit.

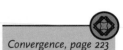

Convergence, page 223

GM Intrusion: *The character attacking the weld comes into contact with the white fluid weeping from the weld's skin and must succeed on a Might defense task or find one hand fused to a weapon, an arm fused to their side, or themselves stuck to an ally.*

For the purposes of combat between vessels, treat wharns as level 6.

WHARN 8 (24)

Wharns are void-adapted behemoths. If asked, the datasphere describes wharns as living battle automatons that fought during a prior age, serving as a first line of defense—though against what isn't clear. An age later, wharn descendants now glide through the airless night beyond the Earth for centuries at a time, as if dead or deactivated. But don't be deceived. For reasons known only to themselves, these behemoths sometimes light up, open eyes burning with deadly energy, and flex claws of particle-beam fury.

Motive: Defense

Environment: Anywhere floating through the void near Earth

Health: 33

Damage Inflicted: 10 points

Armor: 5

Movement: Long when flying

Modification: Speed defense as level 6 due to size.

Combat: Most of the time, wharns are inactive and might seem to be tumbling artifacts. In this state, explorers might be able to partly wake one in an attempt to negotiate. However, if a wharn is damaged, or if the passive senses deep in its body wake it to combat for reasons of its own, the creature becomes aggressive. Because of its size, a wharn can attack large vessels, and because of its discerning senses, it can also go after human-sized targets.

A wharn's main weapons are its claws, which can extend in an instant, becoming exotic-matter beams able to reach a target within 20 miles (32 km). Unless a target is protected by some kind of force field, the 10 points of damage inflicted ignores Armor.

A wharn's eyes can pierce most forms of camouflage, cloaking effects, and cover that is less than about 700 feet (213 m) thick.

Interaction: In spite of their ferocious aspect and war-machine heritage, wharns do not destroy every craft (and void-adapted creature) they come across, or even most. Indeed, sometimes a wharn may attempt to initiate communication via various machine channels. But what comes across are usually nonsense sounds and tones, and sometimes, mathematical formulas.

Use: The PCs, attempting to enter a ruin or structure, are distracted when a wharn attempts to destroy that very same ruin or structure.

Loot: A wharn carcass can presumably be salvaged for dozens of cyphers (or more).

GM Intrusion: *The wharn moves unexpectedly, striking the vessel the PCs are traveling in, which has a chance to damage the craft.*

 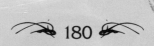

XYST   6 (18)

When curled up, these creatures might be mistaken for rubble from a prior-world ruin, until they unfurl their wings and begin speaking in several different languages, including only those used by machines, at the same time. Xysti are mineral creatures able to control magnetic fields like humans can use their hands and feet. They claim to have lost something they call the Inception Mind in a cataclysmic event. The true nature of the Inception Mind and what the event was that destroyed it, no xyst recalls. In their current fragmented state, each xyst can contain only as much information and reason about as well as the average human being. In other words, not particularly well or much.

The xysti believe they were traveling through the night, en route to Earth, when the cataclysm occurred. Most xysti are consumed with finding out more, finding other xysti with which to connect, and eventually, recreating whatever entity they were part of.

Motive: Knowledge of the past, recreation of the precursor entity

Environment: Almost anywhere, searching for what was lost

Health: 22

Damage Inflicted: 6 points

Armor: 4

Movement: Short when flying

Modifications: Speed defense as level 4 due to slowness and size.

Combat: A xyst can ram all creatures within an immediate distance, inflicting 6 points of damage. However, it can also control metal within short range, causing it to flex, animate, crush, or smash. For instance, targets wearing metal armor might discover they can't move unless they succeed on a difficulty 6 Might defense task to remove it. Or the armor might start crushing the target, inflicting 6 points of damage (ignores Armor) each round until they escape.

Interaction: It's difficult to pick out just one known language among the chorus of all the strange languages used by xysti. But if communication can be established, xysti will cooperate with reasonable requests and negotiate, especially if there's a chance they'll find out something new regarding their origin.

Use: A xyst is found at the center of a crater left behind from a falling star. At first, it is confused and frightened, unsure where it is or what it is.

GM Intrusion: *All the character's equipment that contains metal (up to and including cyphers and artifacts) is stripped away, then used as ammunition against that PC or their ally.*

YLHATH 3 (9)

These air-breathing, degenerate cannibals are likely the remnants of a far more sophisticated civilization of the past. Long-lived and semi-intelligent, the ylhathi have a very rudimentary language, strong religious beliefs, and a wide variety of superstitions. Their leaders are religious figures who interpret omens in everything that happens.

Motive: Hungers for flesh

Environment: Caverns beneath the moon's surface, sometimes in remote areas of Earth

Health: 9

Damage Inflicted: 4 points

Armor: 1

Movement: Short

Modifications: Climb and run as level 4.

Combat: A single ylhath makes a crude but vicious melee attack, or perhaps it throws a hefty stone to attack a foe at short range. In a group, however, ylhathi are far more dangerous. Five of them can attack as a single level 5 creature, inflicting 6 points of damage.

Ylhathi leaders do not engage in this kind of mass attack. A leader always carries a crude implement of religious importance—an icon, a statue, a symbol, or the like. When the leader brandishes the implement, all ylhathi within sight of it are roused and inflict 1 additional point of damage per attack. A group of five roused ylhathi attack as a single level 6 creature, inflicting 8 points of damage.

Interaction: It's difficult to reason with ylhathi, but it is possible to deceive or intimidate them. They fear anything that might seem like a dire omen or an angry message from their gods.

Use: These savage brutes are conducting a bizarre and elaborate religious ritual, and the PCs literally wander right into the middle of it.

Loot: Occasionally, explorers from Earth have found a cypher, an oddity, or an artifact in ylhathi possession. The creatures don't seem to know how to use the devices, but something in their racial memory says they are items of importance.

On Earth, the ylhathi might be thought to be abhumans, but unlike abhumans, there is no evidence that these beings come from human stock originally or have any genetic relationship to humanity at all.

Ylhathi leader: level 5; health 20; Armor 2; inflicts 6 points of damage

GM Intrusion: Four more ylhathi appear from around the corner and join in the fray.

ZANDREL 4 (12)

Weird coincidences are common when a zandrel is near, especially coincidences that aid the creature or hamper or even harm its prey.

This large, birdlike creature has a wicked beak, red and black feathers that end with barbs and spikes, and legs that feature cruel talons. Tiny glowing white motes of light often drift in the air around a zandrel. It has amazing vision and hunts by either day or night, because it can see in even completely lightless conditions.

A zandrel can glide on updrafts in the air for days or possibly months at a time before it must descend to rest or hunt again. It can usually rise so high that it is essentially invisible to creatures on the ground, though its eyesight is so keen that it can clearly see anything that moves on the surface even when it's miles high.

Motive: Hunger

Environment: Almost anywhere open to the sky

Health: 20

Damage Inflicted: 5 points

Armor: 1

Movement: Short; long when flying

Modifications: Attacks and defends as level 5 due to small improbability field

Combat: The odd coincidences that continually plague a zandrel's foes or prey make this creature tougher to overcome in combat than one might initially estimate. In addition to attacking and defending at one level higher than its regular level (because a foe slips as they defend, their weapon partly malfunctions as they attack, and so on), other coincidences are possible, such as the ground giving way beneath a foe's feet at just the wrong time, a longtime pursuer finally discovers the character, and so on. These secondary coincidences are best introduced as GM intrusions.

A zandrel's beak attack inflicts 5 points of damage and stuns its prey, which loses its next turn.

Interaction: Zandrels have animal-level intelligence. They're dangerous, yet some people still attempt to domesticate them, raising the beasts to help create favorable coincidences for their own interests.

Use: A dead zandrel crashes to the ground, coincidentally right in front of the PCs. Unfortunately, its mate is watching them from high above.

Loot: Some believe that zandrel feathers are good-luck charms. And in fact, two or three feathers from a dead zandrel can function like cyphers that decrease the difficulty of the user's next task by two steps.

GM Intrusion: *A coincidence works against the character. Maybe the PC's longtime nemesis arrives on the scene, an old back injury flares up at just the wrong moment, or the character happens to be standing under a statue that topples.*

ZAYRN   1 (3)

Thieving abhumans with extra arms, zayrn are about 2 feet (60 cm) in height with skin able to match the shade of nearby objects. Some call them pesky, but those who've had a run-in with a swarm of zayrn in a dark alley call them vicious. Once a zayrn colony establishes itself in the side roads and eaves of a large town or city, they are difficult to find and burn out. Zayrn are determined to steal anything and everything lone travelers (or small groups) possess—even clothing, if they can get away with it. Zayrn produce a basso drone when they attack, sometimes so low that people can't hear but only sense the noise, which seems to improve a zayrn mugging's odds of success.

Motive: Steal valuables, food, whatever they can get

Environment: Anywhere humans live, in alleys and gutters

Health: 5

Damage Inflicted: 3 points

Movement: Short; short when climbing

Modifications: Stealth and perception as level 5.

Combat: Zayrn usually attack in swarms, ambushing from building eaves high above their targets. If attacking a character to obtain an object, one swarm of three or more zayrn attacks the victim as a level 3 creature inflicting 5 points of damage with claws, while another swarm of three or more zayrn attempts to steal the item. To resist this theft, the character must succeed on a Speed defense task, but the difficulty of the task is increased by two steps (assuming the first swarm attacked to distract).

Zayrn are thieves but will kill those who deny them their prize. Once they have what they seek, they flee as quickly as possible, using their ability to change the color and texture of their skin to slip away as if vanishing.

Interaction: Zayrn create crude nests, almost like vermin, in the heart of human towns and cities. They become vicious if cornered in such a nest, but might negotiate if communication can be opened and valuable items are offered in trade.

Use: Sometimes thieves encountered in the city are not human at all. But one criminal mastermind has "tamed" a colony of zayrn and deploys them in concert with regular thieves and assassins to distract from the mastermind's true aims.

Loot: A zayrn nest contains clothing, jewelry, 2d20 shins, a few oddities, and 1d6 cyphers.

GM Intrusion: The low, basso rumble produced by the zayrn swarm affects the character who fails a difficulty 5 Might defense task, and the PC stands frozen in a wave of dread, losing their next turn.

CHARACTERS

The player characters are likely to meet all kinds of nonplayer characters (NPCs) during the course of the game. Examples include the Aeon Priest, bandit, explorer, nano, town guard, and warlord in the *Numenera* corebook, as well as the arch-nano, deadly warrior, poisoner, and various people of renown in *The Ninth World Bestiary*. Even more often during the course of an adventure, characters meet NPCs that exist initially as someone with a level and maybe a name, especially in adventures that occur in populated areas. Providing details of manner, personality, and interests for these NPCs is up to you. As an aid in doing so, roll on the following table to provide a quirk, a possession, or a motive unique to that NPC. You can roll a few times to make the NPC slightly more complex.

Nonplayer characters, page 269

NPC QUIRKS, MOTIVES, AND POSSESSIONS

1–2	**Possession:** Cube-shaped bauble that floats in NPC's wake, sometimes turns transparent.
3–4	**Quirk:** Obsequious. Overly polite, rushes to comply with every request.
5–6	**Motive:** Honor. The NPC won't stand to have their honor besmirched.
7–8	**Possession:** A cloak so black that even in direct sunlight it seems to drink every last bit of light.
9–10	**Quirk:** Fatalistic. Does anything really matter? Seems fed up with life and permanently broken.
11–12	**Motive:** Paranoid. Is certain that "they" are waiting, and suspects the PCs are part of the plot against them.
13–14	**Possession:** Wears expensive, well-tailored clothing and gives much thought to their appearance.
15–16	**Quirk:** Gossips. Probably knows less of real use than it seems at first.
17–18	**Motive:** Jealousy. Suspects a PC to have something that the NPC alone should possess.
19–20	**Possession:** A pet creature in the form of an animate mass of red slime (level 4).
21–22	**Quirk:** Careful. Thinks about answers, talks in measured tones, seems careful not to say too much.
23–24	**Motive:** Curious. Constant questions about what else the PCs know on the topic.
25–26	**Possession:** A prosthetic arm made of cobbled-together cyphers.
27–28	**Quirk:** Two faces. The NPC has a second, half-formed face that only blinks.
29–30	**Motive:** Greedy. Might be willing to talk, but only for some kind of consideration, usually financial.
31–32	**Possession:** Staff made of light that slowly pulses through the spectrum.
33–34	**Quirk:** Wakes sometimes clutching minor items from dreams.
35–36	**Motive:** Tired. Just wants to get through interactions quickly and without undue excitement.
37–38	**Possession:** A knife made of red ice.
39–40	**Quirk:** Dumb. Even when things are carefully explained, sometimes still doesn't get it.
41–42	**Motive:** Fixated. Obsessed with an unrelated activity, continually turns the conversation to that fixation.
43–44	**Possession:** A belt containing at least three cyphers.

45–46	**Quirk:** Crude. In language and metaphor, the NPC is crude, maybe on purpose, maybe naturally.
47–48	**Motive:** Arrogant. Can't believe the PCs would delay them. "Do you know who I am?"
49–50	**Possession:** A golden hat trailing many metallic and clear synth tendrils.
51–52	**Quirk:** Allergic. Sneezes constantly when within immediate range of cyphers.
53–54	**Motive:** Guilty. Assumes that whatever the PCs ask about actually relates to a past bad deed.
55–56	**Possession:** Necklace carved from aneen hooves.
57–58	**Quirk:** Minor celebrity. Everyone else knows who the NPC is, even if the PCs do not.
59–60	**Motive:** Overly skeptical. It's their self-appointed job to prove everyone else wrong.
61–62	**Possession:** Powder that puts someone who smells it to sleep for three days.
63–64	**Quirk:** Dying. Nothing seems to slow down the degenerative condition from which they suffer.
65–66	**Motive:** Loneliness. More than anything else, the NPC wants companionship and someone to talk to.
67–68	**Possession:** Tiny toy seskii that follows the NPC, though clumsily.
69–70	**Quirk:** Nervous tic. Drums fingers, bites nails, twitches, stammers, clears throat, and so on.
71–72	**Motive:** Loathing. Something about the PCs strongly disgusts the NPC, who wants to get away.
73–74	**Possession:** Circlet of purple flowers worn on the head. On closer examination, the flowers have tiny mouths.
75–76	**Quirk:** Transparent flesh. Their muscles and interior organs are plain to see.
77–78	**Motive:** Money. The NPC will do almost anything if the price is right.
79–80	**Possession:** A green fishlike creature that sings in a liquid-filled sphere.
81–82	**Quirk:** Whenever the NPC talks, nearby insects rattle, chirp, or make some other sound in response.
83–84	**Motive:** Revenge. Someone wronged the NPC, and they want vengeance more than their own life.
85–86	**Possession:** A lizard-like creature no larger than a thumb with an automaton head.
87–88	**Quirk:** Items of the numenera blink and glow in the NPC's presence.
89–90	**Motive:** Respect. The NPC needs to show everyone they are worthy.
91–92	**Possession:** Wears a silver mask without any apparent breaks for eyes or mouth.
93–94	**Quirk:** Never goes anywhere without a sewn cloth toy that they refer to as "Mother."
95–96	**Motive:** Novelty. They'll do anything to learn or experience something new.
97–98	**Possession:** A pendant bearing a symbol that makes people's eyes cross if they look closely.
99–00	**Quirk:** Claims to be aging backward.

"Sometimes we are more open with chance-met people on the road than with good friends. Why is that? Maybe because we have nothing to lose when it comes to a stranger. Sometimes those strangers turn out to be friends we just haven't made yet. So lend a hand when you find a stranger in need of your aid."

~Leverett Stamper

AEON CAVALIER 6 (18)

Aeon Cavaliers started as Aeon Priests but decided to adapt their technological enhancements mostly to martial ends. Cavaliers are encountered with Aeon Priests or in locations where Aeon Priests congregate (such as in the Durkhal in Qi). They're pledged to protect the Order of Truth by exterminating any and every enemy of the Order that arises. Some go on quests to accomplish such goals, or to find powerful weapons to carry out their oaths. Only a few ever achieve the rank of Aeon Cavalier, because to be accepted among their number requires an exacting, difficult, and dangerous trial.

Both male and female Aeon Cavaliers typically wear shining, bulky technological armor with a sealed helmet on which is painted the order's eyelike symbol.

Motive: Aggressively protect the Order of Truth

Environment: Anywhere Aeon Priests might be found

Health: 29

Damage Inflicted: 8 points

Armor: 3

Movement: Short; long with armor-assisted jump

Modifications: Speed defense as level 7 due to armor's force field.

Combat: An Aeon Cavalier's strength and speed are enhanced by their armor. A typical Aeon Cavalier can attack three creatures within immediate range with a melee weapon. Alternatively, they can use ray emitters, detonations, and similar offensive items of the numenera. Finally, an Aeon Cavalier can do any one of the following on their action: levitate 20 feet (6 m) per round via an antigravity esotery or device, turn invisible for one minute via a distortion field, or recover 6 points of health.

Interaction: Usually quiet and introspective, an Aeon Cavalier is concerned first with the welfare of the Order, and then with their own well-being. They might negotiate if they believe that it's in the Order's best interest. They show no mercy to those they believe to have acted against the Order of Truth in any way.

Use: Characters looking for a traveling Aeon Priest find an Aeon Cavalier instead, either one who is suffering from a sickness that makes them prone to paranoia, or one who has legitimate issue with a PC's shoddy treatment of another Aeon Priest.

Loot: An Aeon Cavalier carries two or three cyphers. Their armor is an artifact that provides +3 to Armor and other enhancements, but it is custom fit for the Cavalier and won't long function for anyone else (Depletion: 1 in 1d6 per day of use).

Aeon Priest, page 269

Durkhal, page 148

Some Aeon Priests look down on Cavaliers and believe that despite their oaths, these self-appointed defenders of the Order are wasting their potential.

GM Intrusion: *The Aeon Cavalier produces a cypher that, for the rest of the day, enhances their melee weapon with a halo of greenish radiation that inflicts 6 additional points of damage.*

CYPHER ZEALOT   6 (18)

When a student of the numenera modifies themselves using bits and pieces of tech taken from the ruins, the result sometimes has negative consequences for sanity. Such a "cypher zealot" always operates with a crazed speed and intensity. A cypher zealot can't help but make the best tactical choice, whatever the situation, which leaves a few feeling trapped by the inevitable. Lesser minds, they say, are free to make poor decisions.

Motive: Self-improvement; eliminate other cypher zealots

Environment: Anywhere, operating alone or with abhuman servants

Health: 27

Damage Inflicted: 8 points

Armor: 2

Movement: Short; short when flying

Modifications: Knowledge of the numenera as level 8; tasks related to pleasant social interaction as level 2.

GM Intrusion: *The successful attack on the cypher zealot with an artifact, cypher, or nano ability is turned back on the character, who must defend against it.*

Combat: Every cypher zealot knows that offense is an important part of defense. Thus, they arm themselves accordingly with artifacts and a host of cyphers. An average cypher zealot possesses a personal defensive energy field that attacks all targets in immediate range as an action, as well as a long-range projectile weapon that can reach a target within 300 feet (90 m) and explode to attack the target and everything in immediate range of it as an action.

In addition, cypher zealots have implanted devices that can shield them from view (decreasing the difficulty of stealth tasks by two steps), protect them (+3 to Armor for ten minutes), provide healing (15 points of health), and erase foes' memories of recent events, allowing a cypher zealot to fade into apparent non-existence.

Different cypher zealots probably have a different mix of abilities.

Interaction: A cypher zealot might negotiate, but only if first given a gift of one or more cyphers or an artifact.

Use: A tribe of abhumans was rousted from nearby caves by the activity of "an insane Aeon Priest." Dealing with the abhumans might ultimately require figuring out what drove them from their home.

Loot: At least six cyphers and probably an artifact can be salvaged from a defeated cypher zealot.

HOLLOW GLAIVE — 4 (12)

Hollow glaives often move among regular people, though many times, no one realizes it. They appear like humans who wear full suits of armor that incorporate mechanisms of the numenera. It's this latter feature that gives hollow glaives the semblance of living people when, in fact, they are the dead but perfectly preserved corpse of the glaive who once wore the armor.

Hollow glaives mimic a semblance of the wearer who died, and they may attempt to accomplish the last stated goals of the dead wearer, but without speaking or revealing their faces. It's as if the armor was somehow imprinted with the mind of its former owner, though imperfectly.

Motive: Unpredictable

Environment: Almost anywhere

Health: 22

Damage Inflicted: 6 points

Armor: 3

Movement: Short

Modifications: Speed defense as level 5 due to shield; resists tricks and deception as level 1; resists fear and intimidation as level 10.

Combat: A hollow glaive usually fights with the weapons it carried before life was snuffed out and the armor tried to carry on existence on its own. This means that in addition to swords and spears, a hollow glaive may have a few cyphers and even an artifact.

It's difficult to truly disable a hollow glaive, given their nature. If an attack would reduce their health to 0, it does so only if the number rolled in the attack was an even number; otherwise, the hollow glaive is reduced to 1 point of health instead.

When defeated, the armor shell falls apart, revealing the empty interior (or the long-dead corpse, depending).

Interaction: Most hollow glaives can't speak, though the numenera devices that animate their form have limited ability to reason and interact, and those able to talk to machines can negotiate with them. A few hollow glaives have enough initiative to speak by using hand signals or writing in the dirt or on a suitable surface.

Use: While traveling, the PCs come upon a lone glaive that helps them, perhaps demonstrating trustworthiness. After that, the glaive acts as part of the PCs' group unless they actively attempt to bar it from accompanying them.

Loot: A few cyphers can be salvaged from an inactive hollow glaive, in addition to any cyphers or possibly an artifact it might have been using.

Those who Fuse Flesh and Steel are somewhat more prone to showing up years later as hollow glaives—at least, their fused armor is.

Fuses Flesh and Steel, page 64

GM Intrusion: *The hollow glaive makes a magnificent attack, either attacking all the characters within immediate range, or threatening to inflict 10 points of damage on one character.*

RELEASED, THE 5 (15)

Where they were released from, who took them, and why—all that has been burned out of the minds of the released. Pain wracks them, as do sudden mood shifts that veer wildly between extreme fear and extreme aggression. When the released appear wandering in the mountains, the fringes of civilization, or the streets of large cities, they have a years-long gap in their memories. They're also wrapped in strange metals and synth that are fused to their skin, hiding their features even from themselves. Although they remember their lives before the gap in their minds, the released find that their families have usually moved on after their unexpected disappearance and, just as hurtful, often don't recognize the released for who they claim to be, thanks to the metal and synth second skin that won't come off.

Bereft of their former lives, uncertain what or who tortured and changed them, and without a bridge to a new life, the released tend to become mercenaries or bandits. A few work through the pain and decide to go looking for whatever organization or entity stole them away for so long, only to return them in a mentally broken state.

Physically, the released are more impressive than they were prior to their disappearance. The artificial second skin provides protection, toughness, and additional abilities, though most released would give it up in a second if they could go back to their old lives.

Motive: Defense

Environment: Almost anywhere

Health: 20

Damage Inflicted: 7

Armor: 3

Movement: Short

Combat: The artificial second skin of a released can emit short blades of energy that can cut through almost anything. These blades inflict damage and require that a target succeed on a second difficulty 5 Speed defense task, or their armor (if any) is torn apart and destroyed.

If a released becomes desperate or thinks it's facing certain death, it can exert itself and attack every target within immediate range with a mad, whirlwind display of blades. The difficulty to defend against this attack is increased by one step and it inflicts 10 points of damage to each creature hit. However, after the released makes this attack, it suffers 5 points of damage itself and is stunned, losing its next turn.

Interaction: Once human, the released have varied personalities, but most seek a surcease of the pain that constantly afflicts them, and answers. They'd do nearly anything for a promise of relief for either of these two needs.

Use: While exploring an ancient machine, the PCs find a confused and frightened released wandering nearby. The encounter risks becoming a conflict if the PCs don't handle the situation deftly.

GM Intrusion: *The released's attack destroys the character's weapon if they fail a difficulty 5 Speed defense task.*

INDEX

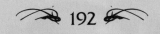

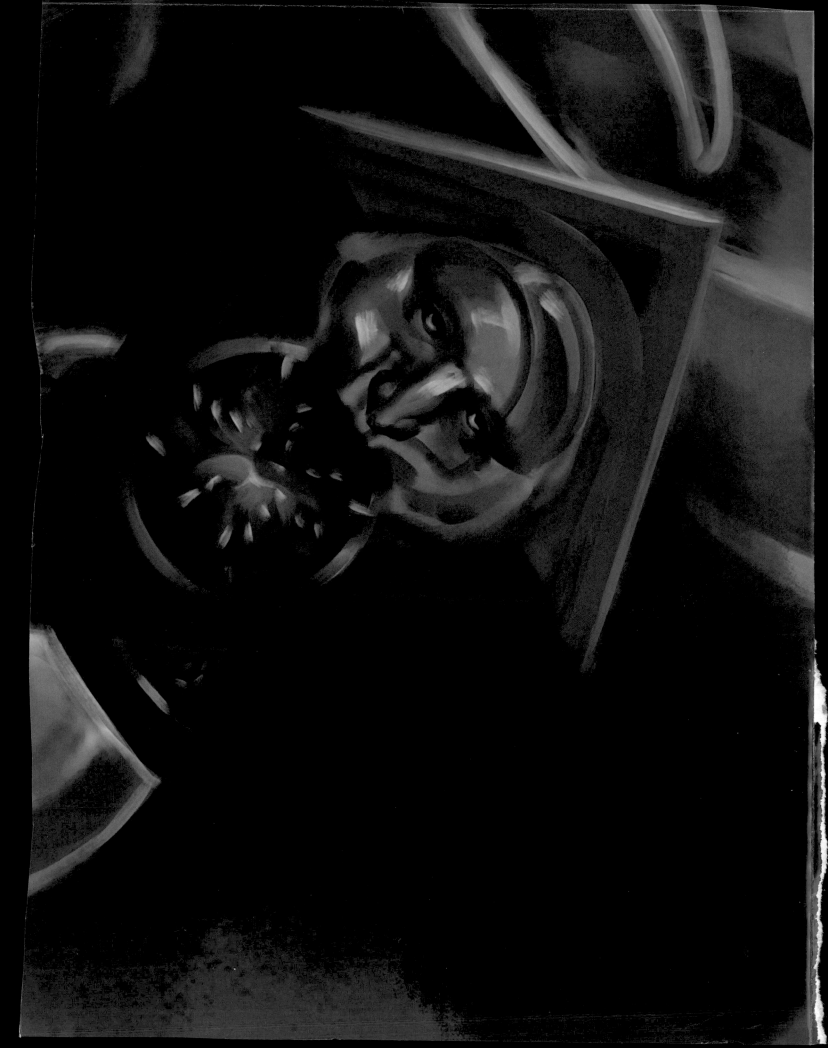

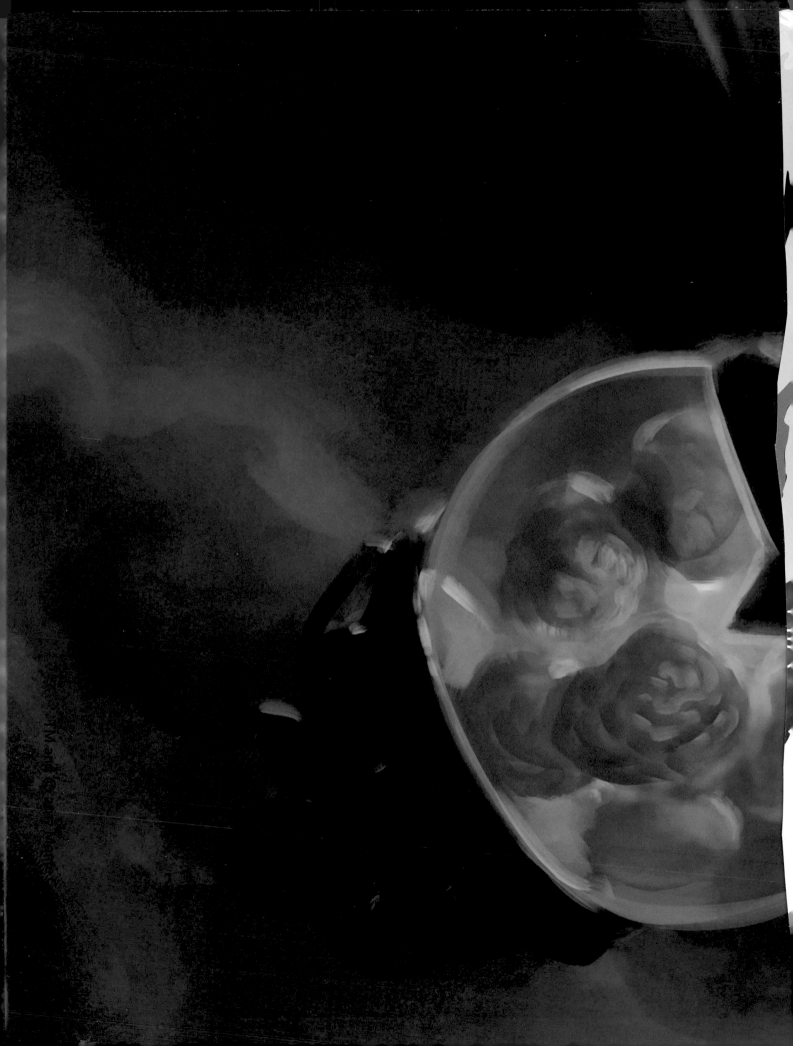

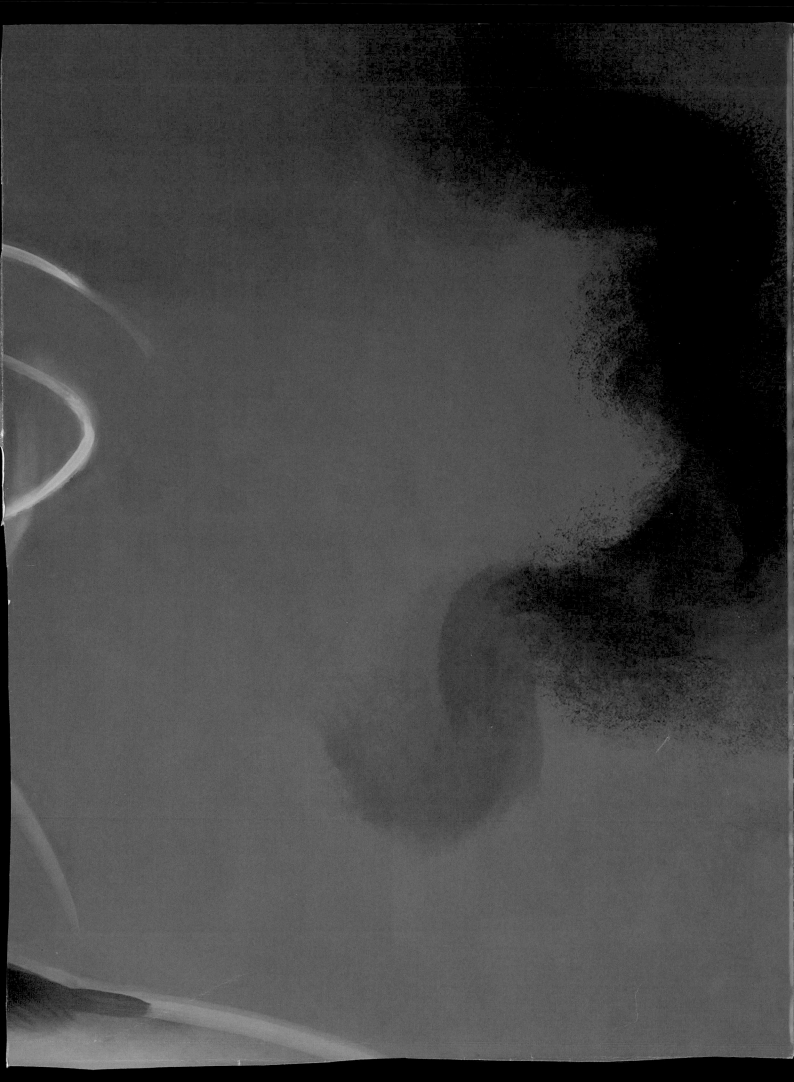

MORE CREATURES OF THE N

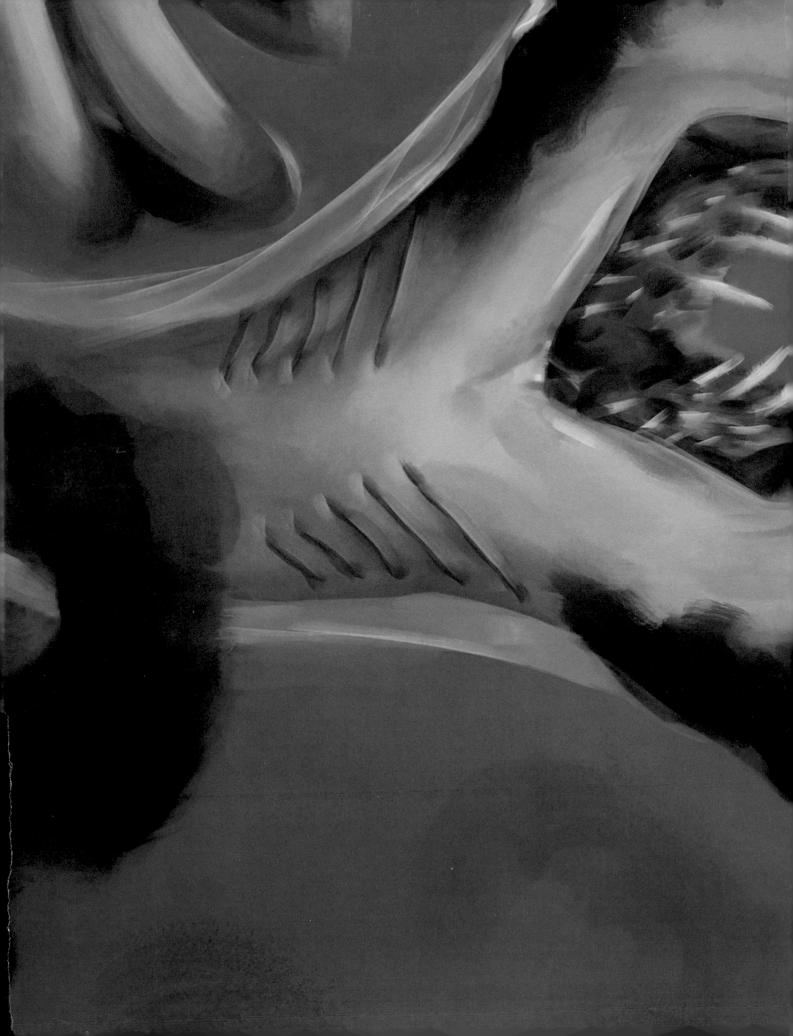

NÉRA™

NINTH WORLD AND BEYOND

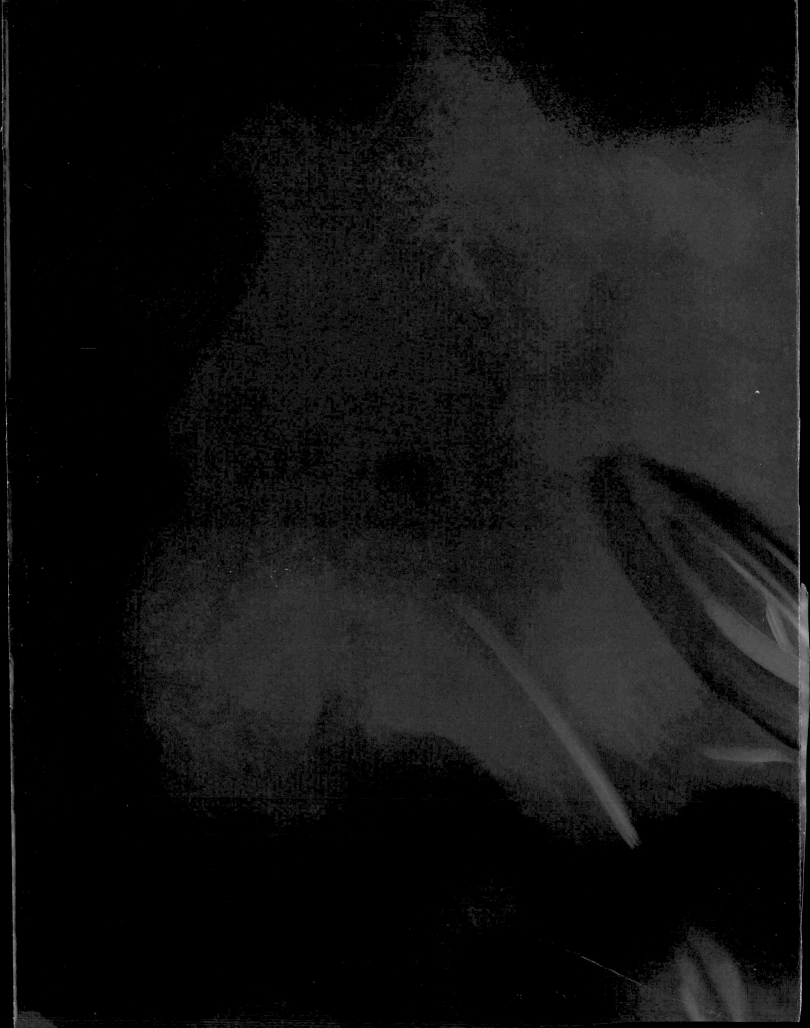